READ 'EM

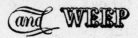 WEEP

L. SheldonPosen
Toronto
Christmas 1971

BOOKS BY SIGMUND SPAETH

MILTON'S KNOWLEDGE OF MUSIC

THE COMMON SENSE OF MUSIC

BARBER SHOP BALLADS

WORDS AND MUSIC

THE ART OF ENJOYING MUSIC

READ 'EM AND WEEP

WEEP SOME MORE, MY LADY

GENTLEMEN, BE SEATED

AMERICAN MOUNTAIN SONGS

GREAT SYMPHONIES

GREAT PROGRAM MUSIC

A GUIDE TO GREAT ORCHESTRAL MUSIC

MUSIC FOR FUN

MUSIC FOR EVERYBODY

THE FACTS OF LIFE IN POPULAR SONG

STORIES BEHIND THE WORLD'S GREAT MUSIC

THEY STILL SING OF LOVE

MAXIMS TO MUSIC

FIFTY-FIVE ART SONGS

FUN WITH MUSIC

READ 'EM and WEEP

A Treasury of American Songs — the Songs You
Forgot to Remember — Some Sad, More Merry,
Some Sentimental; With a Wealth of Amiable
Anecdote, Comment and Fascinating Folk-lore —
A Flavorful Feast of Melodious Music

_by_ SIGMUND SPAETH
With an Album of Elegant Art

Foreword by RICHARD RODGERS

ARCO PUBLISHING COMPANY · NEW YORK

NEW AND REVISED EDITION

1945

ARCO PUBLISHING COMPANY

Copyright 1926, 1945, by Sigmund Spaeth

This book is dedicated to

KATHARINE LANE

the one who least needs
it for she already knows
all the words by heart

*This book is complete and unabridged, and
is manufactured in strict conformity with
government regulations for saving paper.*

PRINTED IN THE UNITED STATES OF AMERICA

CONTENTS

FOREWORD
By Richard Rodgers

ABOUT twenty years ago comparatively few people knew or cared much about America's musical past, especially our popular songs. Then a man named Sigmund Spaeth, who had been a Princeton professor and a New York music critic, wrote a book which he called, in gambler's phraseology, *Read 'em and Weep*. His good friend Katie, to whom he is still married, supplied a sub-title: *The Songs You Forgot to Remember*.

That joyous volume was the first in a long line of researches, running the traditional gamut from the gay to the serious and resulting in a sincere and affectionate enthusiasm for musical Americana of all kinds. Today the citizens of the United States are fully aware of the significance of such materials, not to mention their endless possibilities for entertainment. Those of us who try to write the current popular songs and shows have become more and more fascinated with our national backgrounds of folklore and with all the native habits, customs, costumes, jokes, legends, slang, dances, games, tunes, politics, rivalries and general orneriness emerging from this thoroughly American music. We are grateful to Dr. Spaeth and other pioneers who have helped this country to discover its own history in song. It is a particular pleasure, therefore, to contribute a few introductory words to the latest and biggest and handsomest edition of a book that has also in its way made history and established a national habit. *Read 'em and Weep* is still the gayest and most fascinating of all our song-collections because of its casual and highly personal character. Dr. Spaeth does not hesitate to kid some of the efforts of Tin Pan Alley's ancestors, but under the surface of even his worst jokes there is a patent nostalgia and a clear confession that he really likes the stuff.

Giving the music of most of the songs in a simple melody line makes it available to one-finger pianists as well as to the more experienced ear-players who know how to add the obvious chords. The foot-notes alone are worth the price of admission, and the authentic pictures are as elegant as advertised. It is all summed up in the title: *Read 'em and Weep*.

musical *Cool Whites*, has paraded under the modern title of *Dames*
when this book . . .

PREFACE TO THE NEW EDITION

It is an honor to have a Foreword to this new edition of *Read
'em and Weep* written by the man who best represents American
popular music today, Richard Rodgers. In such fascinating scores
as *Oklahoma!* and *Carousel* he has put the climactic touches on a
job well begun by Jerome Kern and George Gershwin—that of
expressing the real America in honest and at the same time entertaining musical terms.

Read 'em and Weep started out to be a rather sardonic spoofing
of our naive musical past. It turned out to be a record of national
habits and lovable weaknesses that are now enshrined in dozens of
similar collections.

This book has twice been reprinted in the past, in answer to an
insistent and apparently insatiable demand. For the most recent
edition the Preface observed that since its first publication "many
tears and laughs have passed under the bridges of our most super-
cilious noses. Reviving old songs has become an American habit,
and with all the spoofing there is mingled an honest feeling of sentimentality, a truly sympathetic appreciation of how they felt and
acted before the turn of the century."

This new version adds a chapter, besides the Rodgers Foreword,
which tentatively brings *Read 'em and Weep* up to date. It recog-
nizes various opinions and statements, as of 1926, which are no
longer valid, but without attempting to correct them. Things are
different today, not only in our popular music, but in our whole
attitude toward the America so completely expressed in the hit
songs of every generation.

It will be easy for anyone to pick flaws in this record of "the
songs you forgot to remember." There have been new developments
in the scholarly research on *The Star Spangled Banner* and *Yankee
Doodle*. (This author has discovered more than thirty sets of words
to the former tune.) *Turkey in the Straw* has been given a fairly
definite date and authorship. *The Man on the Flying Trapeze* went
through the conventional process of contemporary plugging, and
The Lone Fish Ball became *One Meat Ball* in a daring raid upon the
public domain. Even *Buffalo Gals*, originally *Lubly Fan*, by the

minstrel Cool White, has paraded under the modern title of *Dance with a Dolly*. Franklin P. Adams (F.P.A.) is no longer of the New York *World* or *Herald-Tribune* or *Post*, but an ornament of radio's *Information Please*, while a few others who were very much alive when this book was first written are no longer with us.

Loose ends will be picked up by the author eventually in a far more exhaustive *History of Popular Music in America*, commissioned by Random House, New York. This Preface can best close with a quotation from that of ten years ago, when the continued vitality of this book would scarcely have been suspected: "If there are still a few thousand nostalgic souls who missed the earlier editions, or who have arrived at an age when they can enjoy old songs with sincerity and enthusiasm, or perhaps even a few whose original copies of *Read 'em and Weep* are so well worn that they need to be replaced, the author will be quite frankly delighted and amply repaid."

Westport, Conn.
May 8, 1945   SIGMUND SPAETH

ACKNOWLEDGMENTS

A number of our leading music publishers actively cooperated in the original edition of this book, courteously permitting the use of material from their catalogues, in addition to supplying valuable information concerning the songs. A blanket acknowledgment was made at the time, and this is now repeated, with certain changes and corrections to bring the record up to date.

Several publishers have changed addresses, in some cases even the firm names. The revised list now stands as follows, with the continued appreciation of the author hereby once more expressed: Oliver Ditson Co., Boston (now affiliated with Theodore Presser, Philadelphia); Leo Feist, Inc., 1619 Broadway, New York; J. Fischer & Bro., 119 West 40th St., New York; Harms, Inc., 1250 Sixth Ave., New York; Chas. K. Harris Music Publishing Co. (now affiliated with Southern Music Publishing Co.), 1619 Broadway, New York; Edw. B. Marks Music Co. (formerly Jos. W. Stern & Co.), RCA Building, New York; Paull-Pioneer Music Corporation (formerly Pioneer Music Publishing Co.), 1657 Broadway, New York; Wm. A. Pond & Co., Ridgefield, N. J.; Harry von Tilzer Music Publishing Co., 1697 Broadway, New York; M. Witmark & Sons, 1250 Sixth Ave., New York.

Shapiro, Bernstein & Co., 1270 Sixth Ave., New York, are now owners of the copyright of *Casey Jones*, as indicated in a footnote to that song. They should also be given the following credit in connection with the quotation from *Good-bye, Dolly Gray:* Copyright 1900 by The Morse Music Co. Copyright renewed. By permission of Shapiro, Bernstein & Co.

The Jerry Vogel Music Co. Inc., 114 West 44th St., New York, now owns the copyright of *Two Little Girls in Blue*, which is quoted by special permission. The Southern Music Publishing Co., 1619 Broadway, New York, has kindly confirmed the permissions originally given by Charles K. Harris for the use of his songs. A line of acknowledgment still goes to the *Saturday Evening Post*, which at one time printed some of the material appearing in this book.

READ 'EM AND WEEP

The Songs You Forgot to Remember

THAT line about making the songs of a people and forgetting about the laws applies quite nicely to these United States of America (first and last stanzas only). Besides, there is more money in song-writing if you are lucky enough to have done it before the radio came in.

Actually the history of American manners, morals, tastes, and absurdities is largely written in our songs. Each generation seems to have put into musical form the current sentimentality, whether it dealt with death, or seduction, or mere innocuous love-making on general principles, and the day's extreme of daring or vulgarity as well. Both words and music kept pace with the spirit of the time, and whatever was typical of the contemporary heroes and heroines, the up-to-the-minute beaus and belles, found its way into melodic utterance.

But throughout this musical march of America's habits and conventions, certain basic ideas of song-writing seem to have persisted right up to the present, indicating a stubborn adherence to perhaps mistaken but nevertheless clearly defined ideals, regardless of the laws of grammar or prosody, and ignoring all but a few of the facts of existence.

So far as the music is concerned, the chief theories of the American school of song-writing have been as follows:

(1) That the ideal structure for a popular song is that of a verse and chorus, of which only the chorus really matters.

(2) That a tune which suggests or definitely imitates one which has already been popular has just that much more chance of success.

(3) That waltz time is the perfect expression of sentiment.

(4) That putting the verse part in some different rhythmic form will accentuate the delightfulness of the waltz time.

1

(5) That a cadence with barber-shop harmony inserted here and there will bring tears to the most hardened eyes.

(6) That an occasional chance to hang on to a long note, even on an unimportant word like "of," is not to be overlooked.

(7) That the human mind is incapable of retaining any but the simplest melodic intervals, and the human voice of singing beyond the limits of one octave.

On the side of the words, the following principles are important:

(1) Correctness of English is by no means an asset, and may at times be a positive handicap.

(2) Assonance is often to be preferred to rhyme. So long as the vowel sounds are the same, what's the difference?

(3) The mispronunciation of words and other evidences of deficient mentality should always be accepted as the height of wit.

(4) Correct accenting is a trifling matter as compared with hifalutin artificiality of language.

(5) The world is full of wronged women and malevolent villains and something should be done about it.

(6) Death should always be the occasion for a maudlin orgy, increasing in volume according to the extreme youth or extreme age of the victim.

(7) Sin is wrong; virtue is most praiseworthy; gold is a highly overrated commodity; marriage may be achieved under almost any circumstances, even on the spur of the moment; and no matter how desperate the situation, evil cannot possibly triumph.

With these fundamentals consistently emphasized, certain songs have stood out from time to time and actually made history or coöperated with it. They deserve some fairly serious analysis, as well as an occasional reflection of a less serious nature, and they reveal much of human nature, quite apart from their specific application to American society.

"Read 'em and weep," or laugh, as the case may be. And if you don't believe it, look up the originals, for these things actually happened.

EARLY EFFORTS

In the days when the United States of America were just finding themselves as a nation, the prevailing type of popular song was naturally patriotic. A few tunes served for a variety of texts, and most of this melodic material was imported from England.

Whatever lay beyond the pale of patriotism and politics was likely to be in romantic or sentimental vein, full of high-sounding phrases, moral precepts, and elegant allusions, particularly to mythology.

The English, though artificial, was generally good, and there were standards of rhyme and metre in keeping with those of the more serious poetry of the day. Folk-song, as such, had practically no existence in the America of 1780–1830 (except for the native music of the Indians), and popular tunes sprang chiefly from the drawing rooms, where, usually borrowed from abroad, they were made to fit almost any occasion.

The note of comedy was conspicuously absent, and what passed for comedy really wasn't at all.

YANKEE DOODLE

"But," says the First Reader, "*Yankee Doodle* is far from a forgotten song. In fact, it is the most familiar of all American songs." And quite right, too, so far as the tune is concerned. But how many people know any of the words beyond the conventional chorus? And how many are aware of the real antiquity of this musical concoction, which started as an actual folk-song, developed into a crude joke, and ended as a national institution, with the final blessing of George Cohan himself?

The version of *Yankee Doodle* that most of us know runs about as follows:

> Yankee Doodle came[1] to town,
>   A-riding on a pony,
> He stuck a feather in his hat
>   And called it macaroni.

[1] Or "went."

3

Yankee Doodle, keep it up,
Yankee Doodle dandy,
Mind the music and the step,
And with the girls be handy.

The origin of this doggerel dates all the way back to the time of Oliver Cromwell. After the uprising against King Charles I, the future Protector is said to have entered Oxford on a small horse, wearing a single plume, fastened with a knot, jocularly known as a "macaroni."

The Cavaliers laughed themselves to death over this amusing situation, and made up the words on which the American version is based:

Yankee Doodle came to town
Upon a Kentish pony;
He stuck a feather in his cap,
Upon a macaroni.

But the melody was a much earlier affair. It had long been sung in England as a nursery rhyme, which is still heard occasionally:

Lucy Locket lost her pocket,
Kitty Fisher found it—
Nothing in it, nothing on it,
But the binding round it.

Where and when the tune actually began is still a comparative mystery. In southern France they claim it as an ancient vintage song. In Holland it was used as a reapers' song, with the words:

Yanker, dudel, doodle down,
Diddle, dudel, lanther,
Yanke viver, voover vown,
Botermilk und tanther.[1]

---

[1]The significance of the words seems to be that the labourers received as wages "as much buttermilk as they could drink, and a tenth of the grain." See the discussion of *Yankee Doodle* in "Our Familiar Songs and Those Who Made Them," edited by H. K. Johnson, Henry Holt & Co., 1909.

It has also been called at various times a "popular air of Biscay," a "sword-dance, played on solemn occasions by the people of San Sebastian," an air which "certainly has its origin in the music of the free Pyrenees," and "the heroic Danza Esparta of brave old Biscay."

The introduction of *Yankee Doodle* to America, however, is by no means shrouded in doubt. In June of the year 1755, General Braddock of the British Army was gathering Colonial soldiers near Albany for an attack upon the French and Indians at Niagara and Frontenac. The appearance of the "old continentals in their ragged regimentals" appealed to our aristocratic forefathers as a huge joke, and immediately called to mind the traditional picture of Cromwell riding on his pony.

A certain Dr. Richard Shuckburg, the regimental surgeon, suited the word to the action, wrote down the time-honoured parody, with its nursery tune, and gave it to the band as "the latest martial music of merry England." It was immediately taken up in all seriousness, and twenty-five years later the same tune sounded in the ears of Cornwallis as he gave up his sword at Yorktown.

The complete text, as given below, was evidently the gradual accumulation of military and civilian wit, and of course there were stanzas, preserved by hearsay only, which appeared only on those boisterous occasions from which ladies (and, according to General Grant, gentlemen as well) were debarred. It is all a rather violent but thoroughly conscious gesture of naïveté, and not very funny.

> Father and I went down to camp,
>   Along with Cap'n Goodwin,
> And there we saw the men and boys,
>   As thick as hasty puddin'!
>
> *Chorus:* Yankee Doodle, keep it up,
>   Yankee Doodle dandy,
> Mind the music and the step,
>   And with the girls be handy!
>
> And there we see a thousand men,
>   As rich as Squire David;
> And what they wasted ev'ry day,
>   I wish it could be saved. [*Chorus*]

The 'lasses they eat ev'ry day,
　　Would keep a house a winter;
They have so much that, I'll be bound,
　　They eat it when they've mind ter.　[*Chorus*]

And there I see a swamping gun,
　　Large as a log of maple,
Upon a deuced little cart,
　　A load for father's cattle.[1]　[*Chorus*]

And every time they shoot it off,
　　It takes a horn of powder,
And makes a noise like father's gun,
　　Only a nation louder.　[*Chorus*]

I went as nigh to one myself
　　As 'Siah's underpinning;
And father went as nigh agin,
　　I thought the deuce was in him.[2]　[*Chorus*]

Cousin Simon grew so bold,
　　I thought he would have cocked it,
It scared me so I shrinked it off
　　And hung by father's pocket.　[*Chorus*]

And Cap'n Davis had a gun,
　　He kind of clapt his hand on't,
And stuck a crooked stabbing iron[3]
　　Upon the little end on't.　[*Chorus*]

And there I see a pumpkin shell
　　As big as mother's basin;
And every time they touched it off
　　They scampered like the nation.　[*Chorus*]

---

[1]This and most of the other rhymes in *Yankee Doodle* clearly anticipate the technique of the modern lyric writers.

[2]Strong language, but remember this was an army song.

[3]Unquestionably the author has in mind a bayonet.

And there they'd fife away like fun,
    And play on corn-stalk fiddles,
And some had ribbons red as blood,
    All bound around their middles. *[Chorus]*

The troopers, too, would gallop up,
    And fire right in our faces;
It scared me almost half to death
    To see them run such races. *[Chorus]*

Uncle Sam came there to change
    Some pancakes and some onions,
For 'lasses cakes to carry home
    To give his wife and young ones. *[Chorus]*

I see a little barrel too,
    The heads were made of leather;
They knocked upon't with little clubs
    And called the folks together.[4] *[Chorus]*

And there was Cap'n Washington,
    And gentle folks about him;
They say he's grown so 'tarnal proud,
    He will not ride without 'em. *[Chorus]*

He got him on his meeting clothes
    Upon a slapping stallion,
He set the world along in rows,
    In hundreds and in millions. *[Chorus]*

The flaming ribbons in his hat,
    They looked so taring fine, ah,
I wanted dreadfully to get
    To give to my Jemima. *[Chorus]*

I see another snarl of men
    A-digging graves, they told me,
So 'tarnal long, so 'tarnal deep
    They 'tended they should hold me. *[Chorus]*

---

[4] A more far-fetched description of a drum would be hard to find, but to simulate stupidity has always been a difficult matter. People are so likely to take you at your word.

It scared me so I hooked it off,
    Nor stopped, as I remember,
Nor turned about till I got home,
    Locked up in mother's chamber.[5] [*Chorus*]

---

[5]Another version is:

It scared me so, I ran the streets,
    Nor stopped, as I remember,
Till I got home, and safely locked
    In granny's little chamber.

Here is still another ending:

But I can't tell you half I see,
    They kept up such a smother;
So I took my hat off, made a bow,
    And scampered home to mother.

TO ANACREON IN HEAVEN

Yes, that is undoubtedly the tune of *The Star-Spangled Banner* that you see below, and perhaps you will be shocked to hear that it was applied to at least two other songs, one ribald, the other political, long before Francis Scott Key wrote the immortal poem of which everyone now remembers part of the first stanza. The words of these earlier versions fit the music just about as snugly as Mr. Key's, and the English roisterers and American patriots had exactly the same trouble reaching the F.

John Stafford Smith[1] wrote this really fine melody about the year 1771, and the rafters of many a British barroom rang to its strains before its inherent note of patriotism was discovered. *To Anacreon in Heaven* has been called a "hunting song," but its relation to hunting seems to be about the same as that of the nineteenth hole to golf.

Actually, it was the constitutional song of the old Anacreontic Society of London, whose meetings were held at the Crown and Anchor Tavern in the Strand, toward the close of the Eighteenth Century. The members were musical amateurs, with a sprinkling of professionals in an honorary capacity, and these took part in concerts which were held every two weeks throughout the season, always followed by a supper. It was the custom for the president

---

[1]Samuel Arnold is often given credit for the tune, but O. G. Sonneck, in a complete and scholarly *Report on The Star-Spangled Banner*, clearly proves Smith's right to be considered the composer. There are many slight variations in the melody, which has always, of necessity, been a flexible affair.

or his deputy to sing the Anacreon song, and after that there was close harmony by the whole gathering.

The society broke up in 1786, chiefly because the members felt unduly restrained in their comic songs by the presence of the Duchess of Devonshire, who had had a private box fitted up for her special use, hidden under the orchestra. The freedom of pre-inhibition days, it seems, was never restored.

With Mr. Smith's music, in modern terms, the words, by Ralph Tomlinson, an early president of the society, are as follows:

To An-a-creon[2] in Heav'n where he sat in full glee; A few
That he their in-spir-er and pa-tron would be; When this

sons of har-mo-ny sent in a pe-ti-tion.
an-swer ar-rived from the jol-ly old Gre-cian:

Voice fid-dle and flute, No long-er be mute, I'll

lend ye my name and in-spire ye to boot, And be-

sides I'll in-struct ye, like me, to en-twine The

myr-tle of Ve-nus with Bac-chus's[3] vine!

[2] Anacreon, of course, is the ancient Greek poet (B. C. 563–478) who wrote chiefly in praise of love and wine. He is said to have died at the advanced age of eighty-five, as the result of choking on a grape seed. Thomas Moore translated his odes into English.

[3] Since Venus was the goddess of love, and Bacchus the god of wine, the objects of the Anacreontic Society were unmistakable.

The news through Olympus[4] immediately flew,
 When old Thunder[5] pretended to give himself airs—
If these mortals are suffer'd their scheme to pursue,
 The devil a goddess will stay above stairs,
  Hark! already they cry,
  In transports of joy,
A fig for Parnassus![6] to Rowley's[7] we'll fly;
And there, my good fellows, we'll learn to entwine
The myrtle of Venus with Bacchus's vine.

The yellow-hair'd god, and his nine fusty maids,[8]
 To the hill of old Lud[9] will incontinent flee,
Idalia[10] will boast but of tenantless shades,
 And the biforked hill[11] a mere desert will be.
  My thunder, no fear on't,
  Will soon do its errand,
And, dam'me! I'll swinge[12] the ringleaders, I warrant
I'll trim the young dogs, for thus daring to twine
The myrtle of Venus with Bacchus's vine.

Apollo rose up; and said, Pr'ythee ne'er quarrel,
 Good king of the gods, with my vot'ries below!
Your thunder is useless—then, shewing his laurel,
 Cried, *Sic evitabile fulmen*,[13] you know!
  Then over each head
  My laurels I'll spread,
So my sons from your crackers no mischief shall dread,
Whilst snug in their club-room, they jovially twine
The myrtle of Venus with Bacchus's vine.

---

[4]Not the name of a theatre, but the mythical abode of the Greek gods.

[5]An affectionate nickname for good old Jupiter himself.

[6]The mountain dedicated to poetry (where Deucalion's ark landed after the Greek flood) and overlooking the oracle of Delphi.

[7]This was the London Coffee House, the Jack's of Eighteenth Century night life.

[8]This line refers (quite disrespectfully) to Apollo and the nine Muses.

[9]A facetious reference to Ludgate Hill, where the Anacreontic Society originally met. The line was later changed to "From Helicon's banks will incontinent flee."

[10]An ancient town in Cyprus, sacred to Aphrodite, who was sometimes called Idalia.

[11]The hill of Parnassus was supposed to have two peaks, one sacred to Apollo and the Muses, the other to Bacchus, thereby assuring easy communication and a cordial relationship.

[12]Swinge means "to beat up."

[13]In other words, a thunderbolt is evitable (not inevitable, avoidable) after all.

Next Momus[14] got up, with his risible phiz,
  And swore with Apollo he'd cheerfully join—
The full tide of harmony still shall be his,
  But the song, and the catch, and the laugh shall be mine:
    Then, Jove, be not jealous
    Of these honest fellows.
Cried Jove, We relent, since the truth you now tell us;
And swear, by Old Styx,[15] that they long shall entwine
The myrtle of Venus with Bacchus's vine.

---

[14]A sleepy god, who made fun of everything, glorified to-day in the Mardi Gras of New Orleans and the New Year's mummers' parade in Philadelphia.

[15]The River of Hate, in Hades, across which departed souls had to be ferried by Charon before they were allowed to join that society so enticingly described in "The House-boat on the Styx" and elsewhere.

ADAMS AND LIBERTY

Robert Treat Paine, Jr., son of a signer of the Declaration of Independence, wrote these words to the old Anacreon tune[1] for the political campaign of John Adams. It was probably through this song that Ferdinand Durang, a generation later, found the air for *The Star-Spangled Banner*, which its author had written merely as a poem, with the title "The Defence of Fort McHenry." Durang did the necessary squeezing and fitting, and introduced the national anthem with great success to the soldiers at Baltimore, where it had already been printed in the local *Patriot*.

About the best thing that can be said for *Adams and Liberty* is that its creator received $750 for the job, which in those days was a fabulous sum. Paine has been described as "vain, lazy, and vicious." A Harvard graduate, he married an actress and "was denied his father's house and purse." Nevertheless, he seems to have been the most handsomely paid literary hack of his day.

---

[1]It is not generally realized that this melody served for more than twenty American songs about the end of the Eighteenth Century and the beginning of the Nineteenth. One of the most ribald texts began "When Bibo went down to the regions below." In 1824, there was a song, *Lafayette's Return*, of which the first stanza ended:

    "And the stars of our banner in darkness shall set
    Ere oblivion gather the wreaths of Fayette."

In 1828, *Adams and Liberty* had become *Adams and Clay*, with the corresponding lines reading:

    "With hearts tuned to rapture, let's hail this bright day,
    Beneath the bland influence of Adams and Clay."

There is a story that Paine was dining with Major Benjamin Russell, who remarked that *Adams and Liberty* neglected to mention George Washington, and added that "he could not fill his glass until the error had been corrected; whereupon the author, after a moment's thinking, scratched off the last stanza of the song as it now stands." At that, it isn't much worse than the rest of it.

Adams and Liberty is one of the earliest reasons for the length of political meetings. It is hard to believe that the whole thing could even be read, much less sung.

Here are the words:

Ye sons of Columbia, who bravely have fought
   For those rights which unstained from your sires have descended,
May you long taste the blessings your valor has bought,
   And your sons reap the soil which your fathers defended;
     Mid the reign of mild peace,
     May your nation increase,
With the glory of Rome, and the wisdom of Greece;
   And ne'er shall the sons of Columbia be slaves,[1]
   While the earth bears a plant, or the sea rolls a wave.[2]

In a clime whose rich vales feed the marts of the world,
   Whose shores are unshaken by Europe's commotion,
The trident of commerce should never be hurled
   To increase the legitimate powers of the ocean;[3]
     But should pirates invade,
     Tho' in thunder arrayed,
Let your cannon declare the free charter of trade;
   For ne'er shall the sons, etc.

The fame of our arms, of our laws the mild sway,
   Had justly ennobled our nation in story,
Till the dark clouds of faction obscured our young day,
   And enveloped the sun of American glory;
     But let traitors be told,
     Who their country have sold,
And bartered their God for his image in gold,
     That ne'er shall the sons, etc.

----

[1]Wouldn't it be a curious coincidence if Mr. Paine had at some time heard a song called *Rule, Britannia?*

[2]After all, what's a mere s among friends?

[3]This noble line sums up the entire argument for Free Trade, a Protective Tariff, the Twelve Mile Limit, and the Transatlantic Cable.

While France her huge limbs bathes, recumbent in blood,[4]
 And society's base threats with wide dissolution,
May peace, like the dove who returned from the flood,
 Find an ark of abode in our mild constitution.
  But though peace is our aim,
  Yet the boon we disclaim,
If bought by our sovereignty, justice, or fame;
 For ne'er shall the sons, etc.

'Tis the fire of the flint each American warms;
 Let Rome's haughty victors beware of collision;
Let them bring all the vassals of Europe in arms,
 We're a world by ourselves, and disdain a provision.
  While with patriot pride
  To our laws we're allied,
No foe can subdue us, no faction divide;
 For ne'er shall the sons, etc.

Our mountains are crowned with imperial oak,
 Whose roots, like our liberties, ages have nourished;
But long ere our nation submits to the yoke,
 Not a tree shall be left on the field where it flourished.
  Should invasion impend,
  Every grove would descend
From the hill-tops they shaded, our shores to defend;[5]
 For ne'er shall the sons, etc.

Let our Patriots destroy Anarch's pestilent worm,
 Lest our liberty's growth should be checked by corrosion;
Then let clouds thicken round us—we heed not the storm;
 Our realm fears no shock but the earth's own explosion;[6]
  Foes assail us in vain
  Though their fleets bridge the main,
For our altars and laws, with our lives we'll maintain;
 For ne'er shall the sons, etc.

Let fame to the world sound America's voice:
 No intrigue can her sons from the government sever;
Her pride are her statesmen—their laws are her choice,
 And shall flourish till Liberty slumbers forever.

---

[4]This, of course, was before the days of Anna Held, and not very polite, we think, judging by the stock pictures of Miss La Belle France, in her Liberty Cap.

[5]The late W. J. Bryan had a similar idea about a million men, and the original of the quaint conceit seems to be the scene of the moving forest in "Macbeth."

[6]How prophetic these words have proved, in the building of New York's subways!

Then unite heart and hand,
    Like Leonidas' band,[7]
And swear to the God of the ocean and land
    That ne'er shall the sons, etc.

Should the tempest of war overshadow our land,
    Its bolts could ne'er rend Freedom's temple asunder;
For unmoved at its portals would Washington stand,
    And repulse with his breast the assaults of the thunder;
        Of its scabbard would leap,
        His sword from the sleep,[8]
And conduct, with its point, every flash to the deep![9]
For ne'er shall the sons, etc.

---

[7]Any schoolboy should know that this was the famous leader of the Spartan band at Thermopylæ.

[8]In plain English, the author means that Washington's sword would leap from the sleep of its scabbard.

[9]As a climax Mr. Paine compares the sword of Washington to a lightning-rod, and a very picturesque figure, too, if you follow it from the start of this final stanza.

FREE AMERICA

Joseph Warren, a fire-eating patriot, who contributed to the cause of American independence "by voice, sword, and pen," and was especially famous for his orations on the Boston Massacre, wrote these words, to the tune of *The British Grenadiers*, shortly before his death. The selection of the melody has a touch of dramatic irony, and the sentiments would fit almost any militaristic nation of modern times. The propagandists of preparedness, for some reason, have overlooked this admirable song:

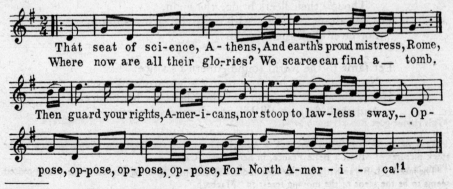

That seat of sci-ence, A-thens, And earth's proud mistress, Rome,
Where now are all their glo-ries? We scarce can find a — tomb.

Then guard your rights, A-mer-i-cans, nor stoop to law-less sway, — Op-

pose, op-pose, op-pose, op-pose, For North A-mer-i-ca![1]

---

[1]Pronounced "Americay" throughout.

We led fair Franklin hither,
  And, lo! the desert smiled;
A paradise of pleasure
  Was opened to the world![2]
Your harvest, bold Americans,
  No power shall snatch away!
Huzza, huzza, huzza, huzza
  For free America. `

Torn from a world of tyrants,
  Beneath this western sky,
We formed a new dominion,
  A land of liberty.[3]
The world shall own we're masters here;
  Then hasten on the day:
Huzza, huzza, huzza, huzza
  For free America.

Proud Albion bowed to Cæsar,
  And numerous lords before;
To Picts, to Danes, to Normans,[4]
  And many masters more;
But we can boast, Americans,
  We've never fallen a prey;
Huzza, huzza, huzza, huzza
  For free America.

God bless this maiden climate,
  And through its vast domain
May hosts of heroes cluster,
  Who scorn to wear a chain:
And blast the venal sycophant[5]
  That dares our rights betray;
Huzza, huzza, huzza, huzza
  For free America.

---

[2]This rhyme goes Brooklyn one better. "Woild" is the nearest we can get to it nowadays.

[3]The rhyming of "liberty" with "sky" is consistent with Mr. Warren's general scheme.

[4]This line seems to be a forerunner of the Milt Gross technique.

[5]A fine, resounding oath, as who will deny?

Lift up your heads, ye heroes,
  And swear with proud disdain
The wretch that would ensnare you
  Shall lay his snares in vain;
Should Europe empty all her force,
  We'll meet her in array,
And fight and shout, and shout and fight[6]
  For free America.

Some future day shall crown us
  The masters of the main.
Our fleets shall speak in thunder
  To England, France, and Spain;
And the nations o'er the ocean's spread
  Shall tremble and obey[7]
The sons, the sons, the sons, the sons
  Of brave America.

THE GIRL I LEFT BEHIND ME

Here is another song intimately connected with American history, although it is of Irish origin. Most people know this only as a grand fife tune, and it has probably marched more soldiers into battle than any other, besides serving as a stock farewell song on shipboard. It was a favourite with the fifers of the Civil War, and still survives through its sheer instinctive genius. There is an English version called *Brighton Camp*.

The words of *The Girl I Left Behind Me* are of unknown authorship, dating back to about 1770. The melody, unquestionably a genuine folk-tune, was "taken down by A. O'Neil, harper, A.D. 1800." It is a great song in every way.

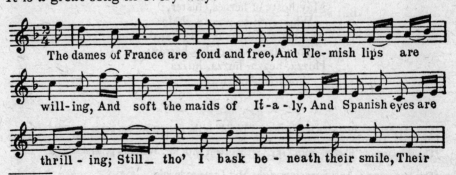

The dames of France are fond and free, And Fle-mish lips are will-ing, And soft the maids of It-a-ly, And Spanish eyes are thrill-ing; Still— tho' I bask be-neath their smile, Their

---

[6]They are not necessarily interchangeable.

[7]There is an idea here that Uncle Sam was evidently not taken seriously enough.

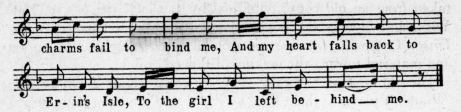

charms fail to bind me, And my heart falls back to
Er-in's Isle, To the girl I left be-hind me.

For she's as fair as Shannon's side,
   And purer than its water,
But she refus'd to be my bride
   Though many a year I sought her;
Yet, since to France I sailed away,
   Her letters oft remind me,
That I promised never to gainsay
   The girl I left behind me.

She says, "My own dear love come home,
   My friends are rich and many,
Or else, abroad with you I'll roam,
   A soldier stout as any;
If you'll not come, nor let me go,
   I'll think you have resigned me,"
My heart nigh broke when I answered "No,"
   To the girl I left behind me.

For never shall my true love brave
   A life of war and toiling,
And never as a skulking slave
   I'll tread my native soil on;[1]
But were it free or to be freed,
   The battle's close would find me
To Ireland bound, nor message need
   From the girl I left behind me.

ZIP COON

One of the oldest of American Negro songs, *Zip Coon*, is better
known to-day as the fiddle-tune, *Turkey in the Straw*. The original words are seldom heard, and the version below is authentic,

---

[1] This rhyme needs no apologies in such surroundings.

taken from an old copy, published by J. C. Hewitt & Co., New York, and now in the possession of Mr. Joseph Priaulx, of the Ditson Company, who has contributed much valuable information and material toward the making of this collection.

The old tune is generally sung to words about a fiddler who "wouldn't play anything but *Old Zip Coon*," and the same idea is used when a text is attached to *Turkey in the Straw*. But why be satisfied with an imitation when the real thing is available?

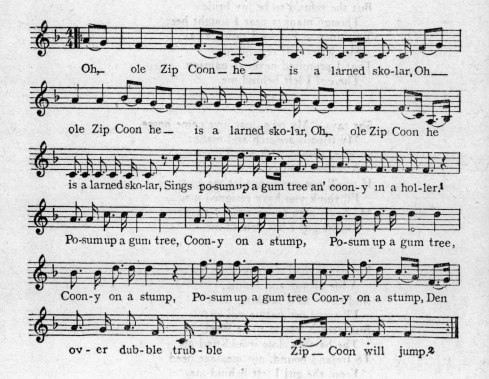

Oh, ole Zip Coon he is a larned sko-lar, Oh ole Zip Coon he is a larned sko-lar, Oh, ole Zip Coon he is a larned sko-lar, Sings po-sum up a gum tree an' coon-y in a hol-ler.[1]

Po-sum up a gum tree, Coon-y on a stump, Po-sum up a gum tree, Coon-y on a stump, Po-sum up a gum tree Coon-y on a stump, Den ov-er dub-ble trub-ble Zip Coon will jump.[2]

O it's old Suky blue skin, she is in lub wid me,
I went the udder arternoon to take a dish ob tea;
What do you tink now, Suky hab for supper,
Why chicken foot an posum heel, widout any butter.

---

[1]The original author is not entirely consistent in his spellings, but he never uses more than one s in "possum."

[2]For a refrain, go back to the beginning and sing the following significant words: "O Zip a duden duden duden zip a duden day," over and over again, finishing at 1.

Did you eber see the wild goose, sailing on de ocean,
O de wild goose **motion** is a bery pretty notion;
Ebry time de wild goose beckons to de swaller,
You hear him google google google google gollar.

I went down to Sandy Hollar tother arternoon,
And the first man I chanced to meet war ole Zip Coon;
Ole Zip Coon he is a natty scholar,
For he plays upon de Banjo "Cooney in de hollar."

My old Missus she's mad wid me,
Kase I wouldn't go wid her into Tennessee,
Massa build him barn and put in de fodder,
'Twas dis ting and dat ting, one ting or odder.

I pose you heard ob de battle New Orleans,[2]
Whar ole Gineral Jackson gib de British beans;
Dare de Yankee boys do de job so slick,
For dey cotch old Packenham and rowed him up de creek.

I hab many tings to tork about, but don't know wich come fust,
So here de toast to old Zip Coon before he gin to rust;
May he hab de pretty girls, like de King ob ole,
To sing dis song so many times, fore he turn to mole.

LOVE'S RITORNELLA

James W. Wallack made this song popular in New York by singing it in a play called "The Bandit." It is of English-Irish origin,
the words by James Robinson Planche (1796–1880) and the music
by Tom Cooke of Dublin (1781–1848).

Love's Ritornella is typical of the sentimentally romantic songs of
the period, and its story of Massaroni the Masher Bandit was doubt-
less terrifyingly fascinating to the chaste but trembling bosoms of

---

[2] The reference to the Battle of New Orleans places the song as early, perhaps, as 1815, or thereabouts.

the 'Twenties and 'Thirties. (Ages or dates, it makes no difference.)

"Gen-tle Zit - el-la,   whi-ther a - way? Love's Ri-tor - nel-la

list while I   play!"   "No! I have lin-gerd too long on the road,

Night is ad-vanc-ing, The bri-gand's a-broad; Lone-ly Zi-tel-la   hath

too much to   fear;   Love's Ri-tor - nel-la   she may not hear."

Charming Zitella, why should'st thou care?
  Night is not darker than thy raven hair,
And those bright eyes if the Brigand should see,
  Thou art the robber, the captive is he;
Gentle Zitella banish thy fear;
  Love's Ritornella tarry and hear.

Simple Zitella, beware! oh! beware!
  List ye no ditty, grant ye no prayer!
To your light footsteps let terror add wings
  'Tis Massaroni himself who now sings—
Gentle Zitella, banish thy fear;
  Love's Ritornella tarry and hear.

Compare with this song *The Gipsy's Warning*, written some years later, but early enough to catch the romantic spirit:

Do not trust him gentle lady,
  Though his voice be low and sweet,
Heed not him who kneels before you,
  Gently pleading at thy feet,
Now thy life is in its morning,
  Cloud not this thy happy lot,
Listen to the gipsy's warning,
  Gentle lady, trust him not.

Do not turn so coldly from me,
  I would only guard thy youth
From his stern and withering power,
  I would only tell thee truth,
I would shield thee from all danger,
  Save thee from the tempter's snare,
Lady, shun that dark-eyed stranger,
  I have warned thee, now beware.

Lady, once there lived a maiden,
  Pure and bright, and, like thee, fair,
But he wooed, and wooed, and won her,
  Filled her gentle heart with care;
Then he heeded not her weeping,
  Nor cared he her life to save,
Soon she perished, now she's sleeping
  In the cold and silent grave.

Keep thy gold, I do not wish it!
  Lady, I have prayed for this,
For the hour when I might foil him,
  Rob him of expected bliss;
Gentle lady, do not wonder
  At my words so cold and wild,
Lady, in that green grave, yonder
  Lies the gipsy's only child.

WIFE, CHILDREN, AND FRIENDS

A thoroughly moral song in every way (with apologies for the pre-Volstead sentiments of the final lines) and a splendid example of the rather elaborate craftsmanship of late Eighteenth and early Nineteenth Century song-writing is this eulogy of admittedly estimable possessions. One falls almost unconsciously into an extravagance of phraseology as a result of merely reading the words. While they were written by a minor English poet, William Robert Spencer (1770–1834), their popularity developed largely in American households shortly after the year 1800.

An enthusiastic editor sums up Mr. Spencer's writings as "principally descriptive of various phases of elegant life. Every school-

girl has wept over his poem, 'Beth-Gelert, the Good Greyhound.'"
(Fortunately, we have not been present on any of those occasions.
But let us admit for the sake of the argument that Beth-Gelert was
probably not merely good but perfect.)

Concerning the tune of *Wife, Children, and Friends* there seems
to be no information available. It is of the rousing British type
and sounds well if sung standing on a table. The sturdy references
to mythology, geography, navigation, botany, and other sciences
are quite in character, and the whole affair is a most eloquent
argument in favour of light wines and beer.

When the black let-ter'd list to the gods was pre-sent-ed, The
list of what fate to each mor-tal in - tends, At the
long string of ills a kind god-dess re-lent-ed, And
slipp'd in three bless-ings, wife, chil - dren and friends. In
vain sur-ly Plu-to main - tain'd he was cheat-ed; For
jus-tice di-vine could not com-pass its— ends; The
scheme of man's pen-ance, he swore, was de-feat-ed, For
earth be-came heav'n with wife, chil-dren and friends.

The soldier, whose deeds live immortal in story,
  Whom duty to far distant latitudes sends,
With transport would barter whole ages of glory
  For one happy day with wife, children, and friends.
Though valor still glows in his life's waning embers,
  The death-wounded tar who his colors defends
Drops a tear of regret, as he, dying, remembers,
  How blessed was his home with wife, children, and friends.

Though spice-breathing gales o'er his caravan hover,—
  Though round him Arabia's whole fragrance ascends,
The merchant still thinks of the woodbines that cover
  The bower where he sat with wife, children, and friends.
The day-spring of youth, still unclouded by sorrow,
  Alone on itself for enjoyment depends:
But drear is the twilight of age, if it borrow
  No warmth from the smiles of wife, children, and friends.

Let the breath of renown ever freshen and nourish
  The laurel which o'er her dead favorite bends;
O'er me wave the willow, and long may it flourish,
  Bedewed with the tears of wife, children, and friends.
Let us drink,—for my song, growing graver and graver,
  To subjects too solemn insensibly tends;
Let us drink, pledge me high,—love and virtue shall flavor
  The glass which I fill to wife, children, and friends.

WOODMAN, SPARE THAT TREE

This song, which lives to-day chiefly in its oft-quoted title, was the work of George P. Morris, inseparably associated with N. P. Willis, with whom he conducted the *Mirror*, the *New Mirror*, and the *Home Journal*, polite literary journals of the early Nineteenth Century. General Morris was born in Philadelphia, October 10, 1802, but his life was spent mostly in New York City, where he died July 6, 1864.

Henry Russell, who composed the melody, has left us this touching story, to prove the power of the words and music:

After I had sung the noble ballad of *Woodman, Spare that Tree*, at Boulogne, an old gentleman among the audience, who was greatly moved by the simple and touching beauty of the words, rose and said, "I beg your pardon, Mr.

Russell, but was the tree really spared?" "It was," said I. "I am very glad to hear it," said he, as he took his seat amidst the applause of the whole assembly. I never saw such excitement in any concert-room.

(Page Mr. Chaliapin!)

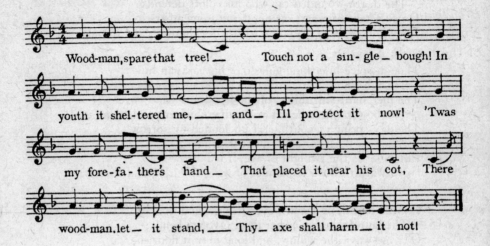

Wood-man, spare that tree! — Touch not a sin-gle — bough! In youth it shel-tered me, —— and — I'll pro-tect it now! 'Twas my fore-fa-ther's hand — That placed it near his cot, There wood-man, let — it stand, —— Thy — axe shall harm — it not!

That old familiar tree,
   Whose glory and renown
Are spread o'er land and sea,
   And would'st thou hew it down?
Woodman, forbear thy stroke!
   Cut not its earth-bound ties;
Oh! spare that agèd oak,
   Now towering to the skies.

When but an idle boy,
   I sought its grateful shade;
In all their gushing joy,
   Here, too, my sisters played;
My mother kissed me here;
   My father pressed my hand,
Forgive this foolish tear,
   But let that old oak stand!

My heart-strings round thee cling,
   Close as thy bark, old friend!
Here shall the wild-bird sing,
   And still thy branches bend.

Old tree the storm shall brave,
 And, woodman, leave the spot;
While I've a hand to save,
 Thy axe shall harm it not.

Some years later (in 1868, to be exact) a popular college parody on *Woodman, Spare That Tree* was written by John Love, Jr., of New York University. Here are the words, redolent with the virility of the hirsute decade:

BARBER, SPARE THOSE HAIRS

O barber, spare those hairs,
 Which sprout from both my cheeks,
A solace for my cares;
 I've cherished them for weeks.
They come in single file,
 As though afraid to bloom;
But still they're all the style,
 So, barber, give them room.

I've reached a Junior's state,
 Its dignity and fame;
And though these hairs came late,
 They still can honor claim.
With awe the Freshmen see
 These proofs of ripening years;
And bow while passing me,
 Beset with trembling fears.

O, give them yet a year,
 The strength'ning sap to draw;
For then you need not fear,
 They'll grow two inches more.
Then, barber, list to me,
 And bend unto my cry;
O, let my whiskers be,
 Not yet thy calling ply.

And when I'm passing near,
 'Twill be, I'm sure, no wrong,
Your waiting eyes to cheer
 With whiskers thick and long.

Now, barber, fare thee well;
The blade put on its shelf,
And ne'er this story tell,
But keep it to yourself.

A MARRIED WOMAN'S LAMENT

There were hard-boiled cynics, however, even in the days of the most artificial romance and sentimentality. A few songs have survived as shocking reminders that the home life of our dear ancestors was not necessarily all junkets and treacle.

One example of this pre-Schopenhauer school is preserved by Mr. E. F. De Long, an old gentleman who coöperates with the Lamson Bros. department store in Toledo, Ohio. He got it as a small boy from a gray-haired aunt, which places it well in advance of 1850. The song is called *A Married Woman's Lament*, and it has many of the characteristics of real folk-music, both in the words and in the melody.

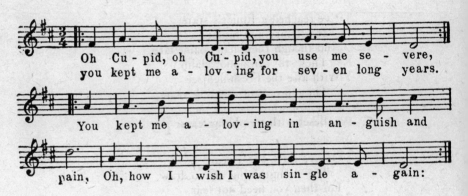

Oh Cu-pid, oh Cu-pid, you use me se- vere,
you kept me a - lov-ing for sev-en long years.
You kept me a - lov-ing in an - guish and
pain, Oh, how I wish I was sin-gle a- gain:

Before I was married, 'twas nothing but love,
'Twas, Oh my ducky darling, my sweet honey dove,
||But now I am married, it's quite a different thing,
Get up and get the breakfast, you darn lazy thing.||

Before I was married, I lived at my ease,
But now I am married, I have a husband to please,
||Four small children and them to maintain,
Oh, how I wish I was single again!||

Washing and mending, we daily have to do,
Ironing and baking must be remembered too,
||House to clean up when spring comes, too,
The young ones are squalling, oh, what will I do?||

One cries, "Mother, I want a piece of bread,"
The other cries, "Mama, I want to go to bed."
||Take those children and put them to bed,
Before their Father curses them, and wishes they were dead.||

Another song, of similar import, also in the collection of Mr. De Long, is *The Sorrow of Marriage.*[1] You can get the idea from the words alone:

Oh! Oh! that ever I married,
I find it a wearisome life,
I see so many examples,
I scorn the name of a wife,
For a bad wife is worse than the devil,
The heart of men can't keep her down,
So husbands take good care of the good ones,
They are wonderful hard to find.

Chorus: Oh! it's sorrow, the marriage, the marriage,
Refrain from it, for pity sakes, do,
You'll find it a silly matter
To marry in earnest, then rue.

When I was quite a buxom young fellow,
My age, it was twenty and one,
I married a charming young damsel
As thousands of others have done.
She was tenderly reared from the cradle,
And in a boarding school bred;
My troubles commenced to creep over me,
The very same day I was wed.   [*Chorus*]

Before a young maiden gets married,
The butter won't melt in her mouth,
But when she puts on the ring of wedlock,
Her note-book she soon opens out,

[1]The editor is indebted to Miss Blanche McCreary, of the Lamson Bros. store, Toledo, for securing these songs directly from their most authoritative interpreter.

She curls her hair in the fashion,
An innocent lad to ensnare,
But if you find a good one,
Just give her the breeches to wear. [Chorus]

THE ORPHAN BOYS

Interest in this song is aroused chiefly by the sprightly nature of the music fitted to an essentially melancholy text. One almost expects a yodelling cadenza. It can readily be seen that such a duet would fit beautifully into any kind of Sunday-school entertainment. Having the boys come from Switzerland gave it the necessary foreign atmosphere, and a chance for costumes.

Our— cot was shel-ter'd in— a wood, And near— a lake's green mar-gin stood; A moun-tain bleak be-hind us frown'd, whose top the snow— in sum-mer crown'd; But pas-tures rich, and warm to boot, Lay smil-ing at— the moun-tain's foot; There— first we fro-lick'd hand in hand, hand in hand, Two in-fant boys— of Swit-zer-land, two in-fant boys— of Swit-zer-land.

When scarcely old enough to know
The meaning of a tale of woe,
'Twas then by mother we were told,
That father in his grave was cold!
That livelihoods were hard to get,
And we too young to labor yet,
And tears within her eyes would stand,
For her two boys of Switzerland!

But soon for mother as we grew,
We work'd as much as boys could do;
Our daily gains to her we bore,
But oh! she'll ne'er receive them more:
For long we watched beside her bed,
Then sobb'd to see her lie there dead;
And now we wander hand in hand,
Two orphan boys of Switzerland!

The real yodelling song of all time, of course, is the German

In Lauterbach hab' i' mei' Strumpf verloren,
Und ohne Strumpf geh' i' nit heim.

By 1870 this had been translated daintily:

At Lauterbach lately my stocking I lost,
Without it I cannot go home;
To get me another at Lauterbach,
To-morrow I thither will roam.

The favourite American use of the tune has been with the words:

Oh vhere, Oh vhere is my liddle dog gone?
Oh vhere, Oh vhere can he be?
Mit his tail cut short and his ears cut long, etc.

There is a delicate sausage verse in this parody, which ends:

"Dey makes dem mit dog and dey makes dem mit horse,
I guess dey makes dem mit he." [Break into yodel quickly.]

INTERLUDE

BETWEEN 1830 and 1840 there was a practically songless period in America, with even politics failing to rouse the vocal cords of the nation. Toward the middle of the century, however, popular music became articulate once more. New subjects were available for song. The joys of drinking were loudly proclaimed, while the advocates of temperance also found music a helpful purveyor of their warning message.

Real, honest ballads began to crop up from the new soil of the Middle West, and the idiom of the Southern Negro gradually became a significant influence. There was plenty of rough humour, too, by this time, and the Roaring 'Forties had their share of noisy ribaldry. Eventually, there emerged the unique genius of Stephen C. Foster.

OVER THERE

George Cohan would perhaps be shocked to find that his famous title had been used as early as the year 1844, for a song "published at Jollie's, 300 Broadway, New York." This simple melody, more primitive even than the bugle tune that sold for $25,000 and helped to win a war, has served as the basis of many a parody and much topical material of local significance. The original words are silly enough to suit the most up-to-date interpreter.

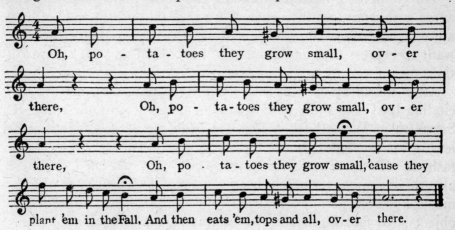

Oh, po - ta - toes they grow small, ov - er there, Oh, po - ta - toes they grow small, ov - er there, Oh, po - ta - toes they grow small, 'cause they plant 'em in the Fall. And then eats 'em, tops and all, ov - er there.

Oh, the candles they are small, over there, [*Repeat*]
Oh, the candles they are small,
For they dips 'em lean and tall,
And then burns 'em sticks and all, over there.

Oh, I wish I was a geese, over there, [*Repeat*]
Oh, I wish I was a geese,
'Cause they lives and dies in peace,
And accumulates much grease, eating corn.

Oh, they had a clam pie, over there, [*Repeat*]
Oh, they had a clam pie,
And the crust was made of rye,
You must eat it or must die, over there.

The words of *Samuel Hall*, p.159, also seem to fit this tune.

FRANKIE AND JOHNNIE

The editor approaches this renowned ballad with a bit of fear and trembling. Not that it is a forbidden subject (although we are inclined nowadays to limit the public discussion of such things to spectacular motion pictures, usually with a Biblical title). But everybody that knows anything at all about *Frankie and Johnnie* is likely to have a version of his or her own, and there is nothing so rabid for righteousness, so bristling with self-defense, as the dyed-in-the-wool Frankie-and-Johnnie fan.

The comforting reflection remains, however, that those who disagree with what is printed below are probably not in need of help anyway, and they can always write to the papers about it if they want to express their indignation in support of any pet stanzas of their own.

After consultation with many highly respected authorities, including Joe Cook, F. P. Adams, Dudley Cates of Chicago, and J. R. Sexsmith of Watertown, a text has been pieced together that at least gives the high lights of the story in an adequately respectable fashion. Two ways of singing the melody are suggested, and here also there is room for much disagreement. The traditions of folk-music, however, permit of wide latitude in this respect, and the main object is to find a melodic line adapted to any rhythmic accompaniment, and sufficiently flexible for all the variations of the text, as well as the characteristic syncopations. Each individual singer can suit this material to the requirements and limitations of his or her own voice, and a combination of the two melodies (and perhaps others) is quite permissible. When so many self-constituted doctors disagree, why worry about minor details?

Thomas Beer, in his "Mauve Decade," places this ballad as early as 1850, but Emerson Hough dates it fully ten years earlier. It is generally agreed that the beautifully honest story is a true one, and that the locale was St. Louis. Later poets and singers undoubtedly added verses of their own, and some of these may be in the present version.

Many interpreters insist on singing the last line of each stanza exactly the same: "He was her man, and [or "but"] he done her wrong." There is a gain in vividness, however, when the line is varied according to the context, and these variations are therefore given herewith. Wherever the language is unconventional, so to speak, the possibilities are sufficiently obvious to the high priests of the cult, and their realization will depend largely upon the occasion and the spirit of the interpreter and his listeners.

Take your choice, then, or construct your own melody from the following:

Frank-ie and John-nie were lov-ers, O-my-gawd how they did[1] love, They swore to be true to each oth-er as the bright stars up a-bove,[2] He was her man, and he done her wrong.[3]

[1] Or "could."

[2] This line is also sung "While the little stars burned up above," and several other ways.

[3] If the variable refrain is used, this line can read "And he wouldn't do her wrong," in the first stanza and several that follow.

Frank-ie and John-nie were lov-ers, O-my-gawd how they did love, They swore to be true to each oth-er, Just as true as the stars up a-bove, He was her man,— but he done her wrong.—

In the remaining verses the lines are doubled up for convenience:

2. Frankie she was a good woman, Just like everyone knows,
   She'd give a man a hundred dollars, Just to buy himself a suit of clothes,[4]
   But he was her man, etc.

3. Frankie and Johnnie went walking, Johnnie in his brand new suit,
   "O-my-gawd," said Frankie, "But don't my Johnnie look cute?"
   He was her man, etc.

4. Frankie went down to Memphis, She went on the morning train,
   She paid a hundred dollars, For Johnnie a watch and chain,
   He was her man, etc.

5. Frankie lived down in a crib-house, Crib-house[5] with only two doors,
   Gave all her money to Johnnie, He spent it on those parlor-girls,
   He was her man, etc.

6. Frankie went down to the corner, Just for a bucket of beer,
   She said, "Oh, Mr. Bar-tender, Has my lovin' Johnnie been here?
   He is my man, And he wouldn't do me wrong."[6]

7. "I don't want to cause you no trouble, I don't want to tell you no lie,
   But I saw your lover half an hour ago, With a girl named Alice Bly.
   He is your man, But he's doing you wrong."[7]

[4]Some versions have "And Frankie bought her Johnnie a hundred dollar suit of clothes," also omitting the reference to Frankie's goodness, and merely repeating that she and Johnnie were lovers.

[5]A curious rural touch, particularly as Frankie and Johnnie were unquestionably city people.

[6]Variations are "barroom" for "corner," and, in the second line, "To get herself a little glass of beer." In some cases the stanza ends: "Are you sure my lovin' man ain't here?" "No, I guess he's gone, With Alice Swan."

[7]Variant: "But I just saw your Johnnie, Goin' down the street with Nellie Bly." (The girl has also been called "Ella Fly.")

8. Frankie went down to the pawn-shop, She bought herself a little forty-four,
She aimed it at the ceiling, And shot a big hole in the floor,
"Where is my man? He's doing me wrong."

At this point the plot branches off into several versions. But they all agree that Frankie killed Johnnie, and that quite dramatically.

9. Frankie went down to the Hotel,[8] She rang that Hotel bell,
"Stand back, all of you chippies, Or I'll blow you all to hell.
I want my man, He's doin' me wrong."

10. Frankie looked over the transom, And there to her great surprise,
Yes, there on the bed sat Johnnie, Makin' love to Nellie Bly,
He was her man, etc.

11. Frankie threw back her kimono, She took out the little forty-four,
Roota-toot-toot, three times she shot, Right through that hardwood door,
She shot her man, Because he done her wrong.

There is a considerable difference of detail in parallel stanzas, as follows:

9. Frankie went down to the hop-joint, Looked in the window so high,
There she saw her lovin' Johnnie, A-lovin' up Nellie Bly,
He was her man, etc.

10. Frankie went back to the hop-joint, She didn't go there for fun,
'Cause under her gingham apron[9] She toted a forty-four gun.
He was her man, etc.

11. Johnnie he grabbed off his Stetson,[10] "O-my-gawd, Frankie, don't shoot!"
But Frankie put her finger on the trigger, And the gun went roota-toot-toot,
For he was her man, etc.

From here on, it is merely a question of how long you want to drag it out, and many of these closing comments are undoubtedly

---

[8] Or some other two-syllable word.

[9] Probably a euphemism for the standard kimono.

[10] There is a suggestion of a cowboy version here; but another St. Louis ballad, *King Brady,* also has its hero die in his Stetson, so perhaps it was the fashion. Still another hero of this school was *Stack O'Lee,* who had both a song and a Mississippi steamer named for him.

spurious. **The** next two stanzas, however, are necessary to round off the story.

12. "Roll me over easy, Roll me over slow,
    Roll me over easy, boys, 'Cause my wounds they hurt me so.
    But I was your man, And I done you wrong."

13. "Bring out your rubber-tired carriage, Bring out your rubber-tired hack,
    I'm goin' to take my man to the cemetery, And I ain't a-goin' to bring him back,
    For he was my man, And he done me wrong."

The suggestion of cowboy atmosphere is evident again in the twelfth stanza. Another version of twelve and thirteen follows:

12. "Oh, roll me over easy, Oh, roll me over slow,
    Roll me on my right side, honey, Where the bullets ain't hurting me so.
    You've shot your man, But he done you wrong."

13. Oh, bring on your rubber-tired hearses, Oh, bring on your rubber-tired hacks,
    They're takin' your Johnnie to the buryin'-ground, And they won't bring a bit of him back,[11]
    He was your man, etc.

Pupils who have done their home work may stop here. **The** rest is purely elective:

14. Oh, bring 'round a thousand policemen, Bring 'em around to-day,
    To lock me in that dungeon, And throw the key away,
    I shot my man, 'Cause he done me wrong.

15. Yes, put me in that dungeon, Oh, put me in that cell,
    Put me where the northeast wind Blows from the southeast corner of hell
    I shot my man, etc.

16. I've saved up a little bit of money, I'll save up a little bit more,
    I'll send it all to his widow, And say it's from the woman next door.
    He was my man, etc.

17. Frankie went to Mrs. Halcomb,[12] She fell down on her knees,
    She said, "Mrs. Halcomb, forgive me, Forgive me, if you please,
    For I've killed my man, But he done me wrong."

---

[11] In some versions this line is far more specific.

[12] There is no clue to Mrs. Halcomb's identity. Probably she was the lady who ran the hotel.

18.   "Forgive you, Frankie darling, Forgive you I never can,
      Forgive you, Frankie darling, For killing your only man?
          For he was your man, Though he done you wrong."

19.   Frankie went to his coffin, She looked down on his face,
      She said "O Lord, have mercy on me, I wish I could take his place.
          He was my man," etc.

20.   Frankie she heard a rumbling, Away down in the ground,
      Perhaps it was little Johnnie, Where she had shot him down,
          He was her man, etc.

21.   Johnnie he was a gambler, He gambled for the gain,
      The very last words he ever said Were "High, low, jack, and the game."
          He was her man, etc.

22.   Frankie she said to the warden, "What are they goin' to do?"
      The warden he said to Frankie, "It's the electric chair for you.
          You shot your man, Though he done you wrong."

23.   The sheriff came 'round in the morning, And said it was all for the best,
      He said her lover Johnnie Was nothin' but a gawdam pest.
          He was her man, etc.

24.   The judge said to the jury, "It's as plain as plain can be.
      This woman shot her lover.   It's murder in the second degree.
          He was her man," etc.

25.   Now it was not murder in the second degree, And was not murder in the
          third,
      This woman simply dropped her man Like a hunter drops a bird.
          He was her man, etc.

26.   Frankie she sits in the parlor, Underneath the electric[13] fan,
      Telling her little grandchildren[14] To beware of the gawdam man,
          "He'll do you wrong, Just as sure as you're born."

27.   This story has no moral, This story has no end,
      This story only goes to show That there ain't no good in men,
          He was her man, And he done her wrong.

_____

[13]With the accent on the first syllable.

[14]Sometimes the grandchildren become merely a "little sister." There is also a verse to the effect
that Frankie was electrocuted, but the happy ending seems preferable.

WATER BOY

Frankie and Johnnie cannot be credited with much musical value, interesting as it may be as an authentic piece of folk-lore and a classic of American balladry. But there were other songs of the underworld that had a significance far beyond that of their text and background. At the top of the list stands the Negro convict lament, *Water Boy*, which has lately become a stand-by with concert singers of all kinds.

The song is already too familiar to require quotation, but it may be worth noting that its music shows a curious relationship with other folk-songs of the world. The first part, consisting of the convict's call for the water-boy, is a universal snatch of melody that appears in an ancient Jewish marriage song, an American Indian tune, César Cui's *Orientale*, Tschaikowsky's *Marche Slav*, and a Liszt Hungarian Rhapsody. The second part, boasting of the might of the convict's hammer, and later denouncing the Jack of Diamonds for its evil ways, is the duplicate of an old Bohemian melody, which Jerome Kern unconsciously imitated in his *Till the Clouds Roll By*, some years ago.

OLD ROSIN, THE BEAU

This must have been a very popular song throughout the middle of the Nineteenth Century, for its melody was used for no less than four political songs between 1840 and 1875. The origin of *Old Rosin* is not clear, but it may have been English or Scotch or Irish, and it probably dates back at least to the opening of the century.

Curiously enough, the name of the hero was generally given as "Rosin, the Bow," and it is quite possible that this was considered a descriptive title for a fiddler or some other type of minstrel. But the authentic spelling is unquestionably "Beau," and there is nothing to prove that Old Rosin was anything more than a popular ladies' man, with alcoholic tendencies.

Here is a correct version of the original, so far as the editor knows:

I live for the good of my na-tion, And my sons are all grow-ing low, But I hope that my next gen-er - a-tion will re-sem-ble old Ro-sin, the beau. — I've tra-veld this coun-try, all ov-er, and now to the next I will go; For I know that good quarters a-wait me, To wel-come old Ro-sin, the beau.—

In the gay round of pleasure I've traveled.
    Nor will I behind leave a foe;
And when my companions are jovial,
    They will drink to old Rosin, the beau.
But my life is now drawn to a closing,
    And all will at last be so:
So we'll take a full bumper at parting,
    To the name of old Rosin, the beau.

When I'm dead and laid out on the counter,
    The people all making a show,
Just sprinkle plain whiskey and water
    On the corpse of old Rosin, the beau.
I'll have to be buried, I reckon,
    And the ladies will all want to know,
And they'll lift up the lid of my coffin,
    Saying, "Here lies old Rosin, the beau."

Oh! when to my grave I am going,
    The children will all want to go;
They'll run to the doors and the windows,
    Saying, "There goes old Rosin, the beau."
Then pick me out six trusty fellows,
    And let them all stand in a row,
And dig a big hole in a circle,
    And in it toss Rosin, the beau.

Then shape me out two little donochs,[1]
    Place one at my head and my toe,
And do not forget to scratch on it
    The name of old Rosin, the beau.
Then let those six trusty good fellows,
    Oh! let them all stand in a row,
And take down that big bellied bottle,[2]
    And drink to old Rosin, the beau.

In the presidential campaign of 1844, James K. Polk, the first "dark horse" in American politics, was elected over Henry Clay, the Whig candidate, by a narrow margin. It had been expected that Martin Van Buren would get the Democratic nomination, but he ruined his chances with a letter opposing the annexation of Texas, and the Baltimore convention stampeded on the ninth ballot for Polk, who had not even been mentioned until the preceding round.

The Whigs set two of their campaign songs, *The Mill-Boy of the Slashes* and *Old Hal of the West*, to the tune of *Old Rosin, the Beau*, and both proclaimed the greatness of Clay.

THE MILL-BOY OF THE SLASHES

Come forward, ye brave sons of Neptune, Come forward without more delay
And rally around your protector, The Statesman, the Patriot, Clay.

The colors that float at the mast-head, Lo! these are the words heard say,
Should be the credentials of seamen—They fell from the lips of great Clay.

To talk about titles, all trash is, Each candid observer will say,
When he sees the Mill-Boy of the Slashes[3] Transformed to the great Harry Clay.

There we'll hail him our noble commander, Stand by him by night and by day,
At the helm of the ship of the Nation, We'll be safe while conducted by Clay.

There are many who seek this honor, But to such every freeman should say,
You'll first stand aside, my good fellows, And leave a clear field for Hal Clay.

There's Lindenwald's farming magician, Reclaiming his bags for this hay,
Has lately defined his position, And entered the field against Clay.

[1] A Scotch word meaning "drinking mugs."

[2] This increases the suspicion of a Scotch origin.

[3] Henry Clay was called "The Miller Boy of the Slashes" because of his birthplace—a district in Hanover County, Virginia, known as The Slashes.

But he'll soon have occasion to rue it, Whatever the solons may say—
For Martin Van Buren[4] can't come it, When pitted against Harry Clay.

OLD HAL O' THE WEST

Rouse, all ye brave lads of old '40, Rouse, ye Locos,[5] my song ye'll enjoy—
We'll sing of the noble old Statesman, Who rose from an orphan "Mill-Boy."

The son of a poor, humble freeman, In Columbia, land of the blest!
He rose 'mid the world's admiration, Hail, gallant old Hal o' the West!

His name is his country's own glory, As hist'ry will truly attest—
From Maine to the far Southern border, 'Tis gallant old Hal o' the West!

His country now weeps for her faithful, Her wisest, her bravest and best;
Who quelled the foul demon of carnage? 'Twas noble old Hal o' the West.

So, freemen, come on to the rally, This motto emblazons your crest:
"That lone star of Hope yet is shining, It lightens the skies in the West.

Hark! freedom peals far in her thunder, Her lightning no force can arrest:
She drives the foul army asunder. "Hail, gallant old Hal o' the West!"

LINCOLN AND LIBERTY

Sixteen years later, in 1860, *Old Rosin, the Beau* was still going strong, and it served as a tune for one of the popular Republican songs of that bitter campaign that led directly to the Civil War. *Lincoln and Liberty* was its name, and a certain F. A. Simpkins was the author:

Hurrah for the choice of the nation! Our chieftain so brave and so true;
We'll go for the great reformation, For Lincoln and Liberty too.

We'll go for the son of Kentucky, The hero of Hoosierdom through;
The pride of the Suckers so lucky, For Lincoln and Liberty too.

Our David's good sling is unerring, The Slavocrats' giant he slew;
Then shout for the Freedom preferring, For Lincoln and Liberty too.

---

[4] Evidently this song was written under the impression that Van Buren would be nominated by the Democrats.

[5] This name was first applied to the Democratic Party about 1834, because of their "Loco-foco" platform.

They'll find by what felling and mauling, Our rail-maker statesman can do;
For the people are everywhere calling For Lincoln and Liberty too.

Then up with our banner so glorious, The star-spangled red, white and blue,
We'll fight till our banner is victorious, For Lincoln and Liberty too.

CAMPTOWN RACES

Stephen Foster's lively tune of *Camptown Races* also had the distinction of borrowings and parodies, and one of these, known as *Lincoln Hoss and Stephen A.*, celebrated the conflict between Honest Abe and the "little giant," Stephen A. Douglas, in 1860.

The original song is so well known that its quotation may seem unnecessary. But it is always a pleasure to feel the resistless motion of its melody, so here it is:

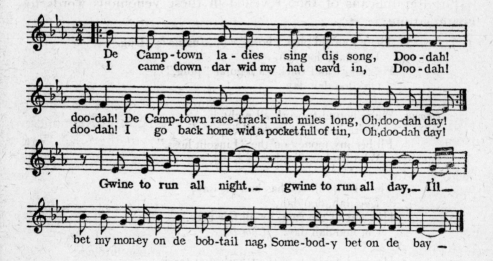

De Camp-town la-dies sing dis song, Doo-dah!
I came down dar wid my hat cav'd in, Doo-dah!

doo-dah! De Camp-town race-track nine miles long, Oh, doo-dah day!
doo-dah! I go back home wid a pocket full of tin, Oh, doo-dah day!

Gwine to run all night,— gwine to run all day,— I'll—

bet my mon-ey on de bob-tail nag, Some-bod-y bet on de bay —

    De long-tailed filly, and de big black hoss,
        Doo-dah! doo-dah!
    Dey fly de track, and dey both cut across,
        Oh! doo-dah day!
    De blind hoss stick'n in a big mudhole,
        Doo-dah! doo-dah!
    Can't touch de bottom wid a ten feet pole,
        Oh! doo-dah day! [*Chorus*]

Old muley cow came on to de track,
  Doo-dah! doo-dah!
De bob-tail fling her ober his back,
  Oh! doo-dah day!
Den fly along like a railroad car,
  Doo-dah! doo-dah!
Goin' in a race wid a shootin' star,
  Oh! doo-dah day! [Chorus]

See dem flyin' on a ten mile heat,
  Doo-dah! doo-dah!
Round de race-track, den repeat—
  Oh! doo-dah day!
I win my money on de bob-tail nag,
  Doo-dah! doo-dah!
I keep my money in an old tow bag,
  Oh! doo-dah day! [Chorus]

"LINCOLN HOSS" AND STEPHEN A.

The Republicans of 1860 revelled in these venomous words to Foster's tune:

There's an old plow "hoss" whose name is "Dug."
  Doo-dah, doo-dah,
He's short and thick—a regular "plug,"
  Oh! doo-dah day.

Chorus: We're bound to work all night,
  We're bound to work all day,
  I'll bet my money on the "Lincoln hoss,"
  Who bets on Stephen A.?

The "Little Plug" has had his day,
  Doo-dah, doo-dah,
He's out of the ring, by all fair play.
  Oh, doo-dah day. [Chorus]

He tried his best on the Charleston track,
  Doo-dah, doo-dah,
But couldn't make time with his "Squatter Jack."
  Oh, doo-dah day [Chorus]

The "Little Dug" can never win,
  Doo-dah, doo-dah,
That Kansas job's too much for him.
  Oh doo-dah day. [Chorus]

His legs are weak, his wind unsound,
   Doo-dah, doo-dah,
His "switch tail's" too near the ground.
   Oh, doo-dah day.   [*Chorus*]

STRAIGHT-OUT DEMOCRAT

Finally, in 1872, when the Republicans had nominated U. S. Grant, and the Democrats Horace Greeley, a few "Straight-out Democrats" met in Louisville and independently nominated Charles O'Conor and John Quincy Adams (a later member of the family, of course), with the help of a song which once more leaned upon the old tune of *Rosin, the Beau*:

We never took stock in H. Greeley, Though Baltimore took him in tow;
We heard that our leaders had sold us, But we never took stock in that "show."

Chorus:
The ticket that's honest we'll honor, And that's the straight ticket, you know;
We would like to have Charley O'Conor; For O'Conor and Adams we'll go.

'Twas said the old party no longer Was worthy of having a head;
But we'll show the sick soreheads we're stronger, When Liberals and soreheads
   are dead.

Then let Greeley go to the dickens, We'll show him he's on the wrong track;
Too soon he has counted his chickens, For Louisville hurts Chappaquack.

We will never desert the great party That stands for Democracy true;
We'll vote on the 5th of November, For Charley and John Quincy, too.

TAKE BACK THE HEART

This excellent song is by Mrs. Charlotte Alington Barnard, who, under the pseudonym of "Claribel," made herself enormously popular in America about the middle of the Nineteenth Century. She was born in England in 1830, married a certain C. C. Barnard, received some instruction in music from W. H. Holmes, and published more than a hundred ballads, as well as a volume of "Thoughts, Verses and Songs." She died at Dover in 1869.

Claribel's best known song is *Come Back to Erin*, and this scarcely needs quotation. She also wrote one called *Five O'clock in the Morning*, which makes rather a piker out of its two-hours-earlier counterpart of to-day.

There is nothing wrong with either the words or the music of *Take Back the Heart*,[1] and it sings something elegant:

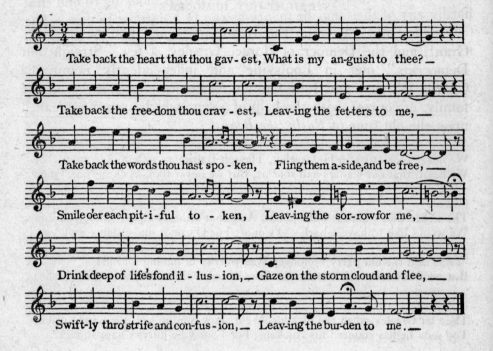

Take back the heart that thou gav - est, What is my an-guish to thee? —

Take back the free-dom thou crav - est, Leav-ing the fet-ters to me, —

Take back the words thou hast spo - ken, Fling them a-side, and be free, —

Smile o'er each pit-i-ful to - ken, Leav-ing the sor-row for me, —

Drink deep of life's fond il - lus - ion, — Gaze on the storm cloud and flee, —

Swift-ly thro' strife and con-fus - ion, — Leav-ing the bur-den to me. —

> Then when at last overtaken,
> Time flings its fetters o'er thee,
> Come, with a trust still unshaken,
> Come back a captive to me,
> Come back in sadness or sorrow,
> Once more my darling to be,
> Come as of old, love, to borrow
> Glimpses of sunlight from me.
> Love shall resume her dominion,
> Striving no more to be free,
> When on her world-weary pinion,
> Flies back my lost love to me.

---

[1] There was for many years a stock joke arising from this line. It seems that a lady (not your own) entered a butcher shop, and said to the well-meaning purveyor of meats behind the counter, "Take back your heart. I ordered liver." This was good for an honest laugh as late as 1897.

The trick of running together a lot of names of songs or current plays, so as to make some sort of sense, is still common in vaudeville, and it still brings a fairly certain laugh. There is a slight shock in finding Stephen Foster pot-boiling with such foolishness in the middle of the Nineteenth Century. It is also shocking to find that hardly any of the songs he mentions can be identified to-day. The Oliver Ditson Company published this curious jumble of completely forgotten song titles:

THE SONG OF ALL SONGS

As you've walked through the town on a fine summer's day,
The subject I've got, you have seen, I dare say;
Upon fences and railings, wherever you go,
You'll see the penny ballads sticking up, in a row;
The titles to read you may stand for a while,
And some are so odd, they will cause you to smile;
I noted them down as I read them along,
And I've put them together to make up my song.

Chorus:
Old Songs! New Songs! Ev'ry kind of song,
I noted them down as I read them along.

There was "Abraham's Daughter" "Going out upon a spree,"
With "Old Uncle Snow" "In the Cottage by the sea";
"If your foot is pretty, show it" "At Lanigan's Ball";
And, "Why did she leave him" "On the raging Canal?"
There was "Bonnie Annie" with "A jockey hat and feather";
"I don't think much of you" "We were boys and girls together,"
"Do they think of me at home?" "I'll be free and easy still,"
"Give us now a good Commander" with "The Sword of Bunker Hill."

"When this Cruel War is over," "No Irish need apply,"
"For, everything is lovely, and the Goose hangs high";
"The Young Gal from New Jersey," "Oh, wilt thou be my bride?"
And "Oft in the Stilly Night" "We'll all take a ride."
"Let me kiss him for his Mother," "He's a gay Young Gambolier";
"I'm going to fight mit Sigel" and "De bully Lager-bier."
"Hunkey Boy is Yankee Doodle" "When the Cannons loudly roar,"
"We are coming, Father Abraham, six hundred thousand more!"

"In the days when I was hard up" with "My Mary Ann,"
"My Johnny was a Shoemaker," or "Any other Man!"

"The Captain with his whiskers" and "Annie of the Vale,"
Along with "Old Bob Ridley" "A-riding on a rail!"
"Rock me to sleep, Mother," "Going round the Horn";
"I'm not myself at all," "I'm a Bachelor forlorn."
"Mother, is the Battle over?"   "What are the men about?"
"How are you, Horace Greeley," "Does your Mother know you're out?"

"We won't go home till morning," with "The Bold Privateer,"
"Annie Lisle" and "Zouave Johnny" "Riding in a Railroad Keer";
"We are coming, Sister Mary," with "The Folks that put on airs,"
"We are marching along" with "The Four-and-Thirty Stars";
"On the other side of Jordan," "Don't fly your Kite too high!"
"Jenny's coming o'er the Green," to "Root Hog or Die!"
"Our Union's Starry Banner," "The Flag of Washington,"
Shall float victorious o'er the land from Maine to Oregon!

FASHIONABLE SONGS OF THE 'FIFTIES

THE revival of "Fashion," Mrs. Anna Cora Mowatt's elegant play, at the Provincetown Playhouse, gave Brian Hooker a chance to dig up some of the vocal gems of the period from his priceless collection. Deems Taylor assisted in their preparation for the modern stage, and three numbers, *Not for Joe*, *Walking down Broadway*, and *Call Me Pet Names*, have been republished by J. Fischer & Bro., in a pleasantly old-fashioned style. They all have some characteristics in common, particularly the interpolation of spoken words, a very smart trick at the time, and still quite generally used on the vaudeville stage.

Not for Joe has something of the spirit of the old English *No, John*, although its protagonist is masculine, not feminine. It is the hard-boiled song of its day, and Joe is surely a tough egg. The rhyming of "knows it" with "Joseph" is unique, so far as this editor knows. The words and music are by A. Lloyd.

Here is this rough ditty, untouched by any refining influence:

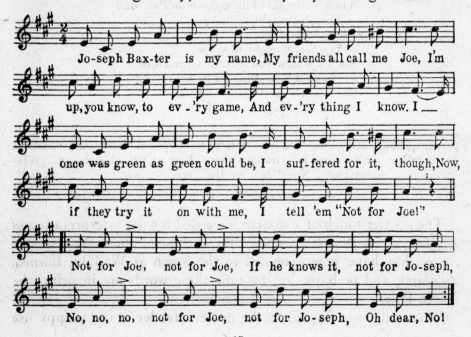

Jo-seph Bax-ter is my name, My friends all call me Joe, I'm up, you know, to ev-'ry game, And ev-'ry thing I know. I once was green as green could be, I suf-fered for it, though, Now, if they try it on with me, I tell 'em "Not for Joe!"

Not for Joe, not for Joe, If he knows it, not for Jo-seph, No, no, no, not for Joe, not for Jo-seph, Oh dear, No!

There's a fellow called Jack Bannister
  He's the sort of chap, is Jack,
Who is always borrowing money
  And he never pays it back;
Now, last Thursday night he comes to me,
  Says he's just returned to Town;
And being rather short of cash,
  Could I lend him half a crown?

[*Spoken*]: "Well," says I—more in sorrow than in anger—"If I thought I might get it back again, I would with pleasure. But you'll excuse me if I say:— "Not for Joe,"—etc.

I think he's had enough of Joe,
  Decline I really must;
He'd thank me for my kindness though
  If I "would only trust."
Ah, "trust" my boy! it's "trust" too long,
  Your favor to retain;
Perhaps now, as you know my song
  I needn't sing again: [*Chorus*]

There's a friend of mine down on Pall Mall,
  The other night says: "Joe,
I'll introduce you to a gal
  You really ought to know;
She's a widow you should try and win—
  'Twould a good match be for you—
She's pretty, and got lots of tin,
  And only forty-two."

[*Spoken*]: Fancy forty-two—old enough to be my Grandmother. And you know a fellow can't marry his Grandmother. Lots of tin, though, and pretty . . . Forty-two. No—"Not for Joe," etc.

The gentler touch of a woman is needed for the interpretation of *Walking down Broadway*, one of the earliest of those geographical songs that have now extended to the beach at Waikiki, Borneo, Zululand, and perhaps, by the time these words are in print, the North Pole.

What will most appeal to the modern reader is the snappy use of that up-to-date bit of slang, "O. K." William Lingard wrote the words of this song, and Charles E. Pratt the music.

WALKING DOWN BROADWAY

The sweet-est thing in life, (And no one dare say nay)— On a Sa-tur-day af-ter-noon, Is walk-ing down Broad-way;— My sis-ters in the Park Or at Long Branch wish to stray, But I pre-fer to walk Down the fes-tive, gay Broad-way. Walk-ing down Broad-way,— The fes-tive, gay Broad-way, The O. K. thing on Sa-tur-day Is walk-ing down Broad-way!— Walk-ing down Broad-way, The fes-tive, gay Broad-way, The O. K. thing on Sa-tur-day Is walk-ing down Broad-way!

[*Spoken part*]: And I must say, Ladies and Gentlemen, with all due reference to other pleasures in life, there is nothing so charming as

[*Sung*]: Walking down Broadway—etc.

Mrs. Osgood's beautifully sentimental song, *Call me Pet Names*, was introduced as a duet in "Fashion," and it should be sung that way to secure the full effect. In its time it held all records for languishing, both long and short distance. If a gentleman and a lady are available simultaneously for the performance of this song, she should do the first verse, and he the second, with the third in close harmony.

CALL ME PET NAMES

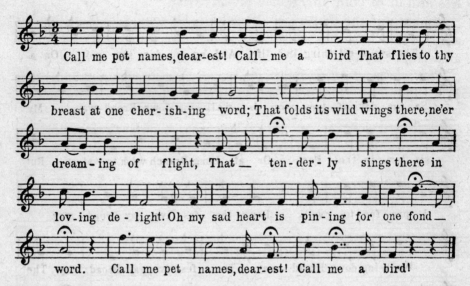

Call me pet names, dear-est! Call me a bird That flies to thy breast at one cher-ish-ing word; That folds its wild wings there, ne'er dream-ing of flight, That ten-der-ly sings there in lov-ing de-light. Oh my sad heart is pin-ing for one fond word. Call me pet names, dear-est! Call me a bird!

Call me pet names, dearest! Call me a star
Whose smile's beaming welcome thou feel'st from afar;
Whose light is the clearest, the truest to thee,
When the night-time of sorrow steals over life's sea.
Oh, trust thy rich bark where its warm rays are.
Call me pet names, dearest! Call me a star!

Call me sweet names, darling! Call me thine own.
Speak to me always in love's low tone;
Let not thy look nor thy voice grow cold.
Let my fond worship thy being enfold;
Love me for ever, and love me alone,
Call me pet names, darling! Call me thine own!

One of the most daring flirtation songs of the period, also revived in "Fashion," was called *Croquet*, but actually dealt with a far different sport. Its cover design tells the story as delicately as possible.

Do you remember the hand-squeezing signals, by which a whole conversation could be carried on in silence? Four squeezes meant "Do you love me?" The answer, in three, was, presumably, "Yes, I do." Then followed two squeezes for "How much?" and oh, how you both squeezed for that final one, to indicate the limitless ardour of your affections.

Looking at the picture, and reading the song, one is inclined to ask, "How long has this been going on?" And Irving Berlin answers, "Always."

The words of *Croquet* are by C. H. Webb and the music by J. R. Thomas. The original publisher was Wm. A. Pond & Co.

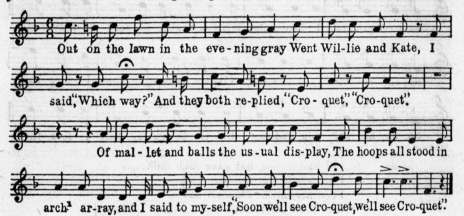

Out on the lawn in the eve-ning gray Went Wil-lie and Kate, I said, "Which way?" And they both re-plied, "Cro-quet", "Cro-quet". Of mal-let and balls the us-ual dis-play, The hoops all stood in arch¹ ar-ray, and I said to my-self, "Soon we'll see Cro-quet, we'll see Cro-quet."

But the Mallet and Balls unheeded lay,
    And the maid and the youth side by side sat they,
And I thought to myself—
    Is that Croquet?
I saw the scamp, it was bright as day,
    Put his arm around her waist in a loving way,
And he squeezed her hand,—
    Was that Croquet? Was that Croquet?

While the red rover roll'd all forgotten away,
    He whisper'd all that a lover should say,
And kiss'd her lips—
    What a queer Croquet!
Silent they sat 'neath the moon of May,
    But I knew by her blushes she said not nay,
And I thought in my heart,
    Now that's Croquet! Now that's Croquet.²

¹Joke!

²Perhaps it was croquet, but was it cricket? is what Indignant Citizen wants to know.

THE LITTLE BROWN JUG

This is undoubtedly the wettest song ever written. Its title has become classic, and is remembered in many quarters where the actual words and music are forgotten. No comments are required.[1]

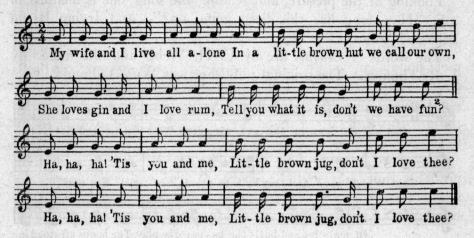

My wife and I live all a-lone In a lit-tle brown hut we call our own,

She loves gin and I love rum, Tell you what it is, don't we have fun?[2]

Ha, ha, ha! 'Tis you and me, Lit-tle brown jug, don't I love thee?

Ha, ha, ha! 'Tis you and me, Lit-tle brown jug, don't I love thee?

If I had a cow that gave such milk,
I'd dress her in the finest silk,
Feed her on the choicest hay,
And milk her twenty times a day.   [Chorus]

'Tis you that makes my friends my foes,
'Tis you who makes me wear old clothes,
But seeing you are so near my nose,
Tip her up and down she goes.   [Chorus]

When I go toiling on my farm,
Take little brown jug under my arm,
Set it under some shady tree.
Little brown jug, don't I love thee?   [Chorus]

Then came the landlord tripping in,
Round top hat and a peaked chin,
In his hand he carried a cup,
Says I, "Old fellow, give us a sup."   [Chorus]

---

[1]William Geppert, of the *Musical Courier*, tells of hearing this song and others performed by singers and banjo players from the travelling wagon of Hamlin's Wizard Oil. This patent medicine made a fortune, one of whose heirs was George Hamlin, the concert tenor.

[2]This phrase, as most of you will remember, served as the title for a modern popular song.

If all the folks in Adam's race,
Were put together in one place,
Then I'd prepare to drop a tear
Before I'd part with you, my dear.   [*Chorus*]

VILIKINS AND HIS DINAH

Originally an English song by John Parry, with strange vagaries of dialect and spelling, *Vilikins and His Dinah* became one of the most popular melodies in America, appearing in college song-books and elsewhere, and often called simply "the tooraloo tune."   (The meaningless syllables of the refrain can, of course, be almost anything.   In the original version they are "Singing to la lol la rol lal to ral lal la," sung to two repetitions of the final line of the music.)[1]

If you are bored with this song, so was your old grandfather, probably, but, like you, he cherished his sense of humour and would never admit that it had even temporarily stepped out.   So bring on your lovers and fie upon him who first cries, Hold, enough!

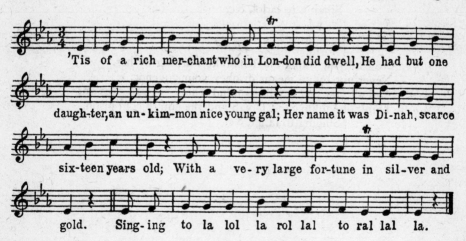

'Tis of a rich mer-chant who in Lon-don did dwell, He had but one daugh-ter, an un-kim-mon nice young gal; Her name it was Di-nah, scarce six-teen years old; With a ve-ry large for-tune in sil-ver and gold. Sing-ing to la lol la rol lal to ral lal la.

As Dinah vas a-valiking the garden one day,
Her papa he came to her, and thus he did say—
"Go dress yourself Dinah, in gorgeous array,
And take yourself a husiband both galliant and gay!"
Singing to la lol, &c.

---

[1]The song as given here is a composite from the collections of Brian Hooker, Mrs. E. P. Richardson, of Houston, Texas, and others.

"Oh papa, Oh papa, I've not made up my mind,
And to marry just yet, why, I don't feel inclined;
To you my large fortune I'll gladly give o'er,
If you'll let me live single a year or two more."
     Singing to la lol, &c.

"Go, go, boldest daughter," the parient replied;
"If you won't consent to be this here young man's bride,
I'll give your large fortune to the nearest of kin,
And you shan't reap the benefit of one single pin."
     Singing to la lol, &c.

As Vilikins vas valiking the garden around,
He spied his dear Dinah laying dead upon the ground,
And the cup of cold pison it lay by her side,
With a billet-dux a-stating 'twas by pison she died.
     Singing to la lol, &c.

He kissed her cold corpus a thousand times o'er
And called her his Dinah though she was no more,
Then swallowed the pison like a lovyer so brave
And Vilikins and his Dinah lie both in one grave.
     Singing to la lol, &c.

Moral

Now all you young maidens take warning by her,
Never not by no means disobey your govenor,
And all you young fellows mind who you claps eyes on,
Think of Vilikins and Dinah and the cup of cold pison.
     Singing to la lol, &c.

RECONSTRUCTION DAYS

AFTER the Civil War, American popular music became more and more distinctive. The Negro atmosphere increased in popularity and to it were added songs in other dialects, particularly Irish and German. The Irish style reached its height in the repertoire of Harrigan and Hart.

This was the time also when the tradition of singing became firmly grounded in the American colleges, and sentiment as well as comedy found expression in the song-books of our seats of learning. There were bitterly sarcastic songs too, mostly aimed at the fops of the day, and the lyrics became more and more definite and detailed as to the places and people under discussion.

Sir Arthur Sullivan's melodies took a firm hold on the hearts of America, even among those who had never heard of his operas. While congregations were singing his *Onward, Christian Soldiers* and high society picked out *The Lost Chord* on square pianos, uninhibited male gatherings had evolved "*Hail, hail, the gang's all here*" from a chorus in "The Pirates of Penzance," and *The Duke of Plaza Toro*, in "The Gondoliers," was serving as melodic background for a heartily obscene version of the discovery of America by "Colombo."

Languishing extravaganzas of sentimentality maintained their prestige, and feminine names were as popular in song-titles as feminine figures in modern tabloids and rotogravures.

"SHOO, FLY, DON'T BOTHER ME!"

This was the most popular nonsense song of the Civil War. It was revived many years later in "Captain Jinks of the Horse Marines," Ethel Barrymore's first play. The words were by Billy Reeves and the music by Frank Campbell.

There were serious discussions at the time as to whether one could feel like a morning star. The first verse merely repeats the phrase "I think I hear the angels sing" three times, and then varies it with "The angels now are on the wing," finishing

I feel, I feel, I feel, That's what my mother said,
The angels pouring 'lasses down, Upon this nigger's head.

The second verse conveys the information that "If I sleep in the sun this nigger knows [three times] A fly comes sting him on the nose." This time the finish is "Whenever this nigger goes to sleep, He must cover up his head." Here is the chorus:

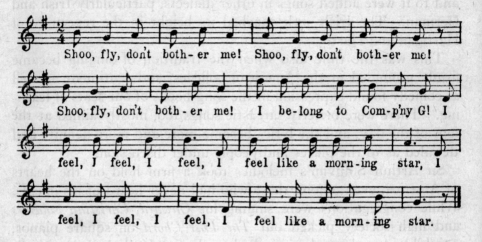

When Johnny Comes Marching Home is thoroughly familiar to-day, while the later Johnny, Get Your Gun is remembered chiefly as a dance tune.

A self-taught Connecticut composer, dedicated chiefly to the causes of temperance and Northern patriotism, was Henry Clay Work (1832-84). According to the picture in Louis Elson's History of American Music, Mr. Work looked like the two Smith Brothers rolled into one, and his best-known song is Marching through Georgia. But he also did Kingdom Coming, which was revived not so long ago by Jerome Kern in a magnificent arrangement, and his Grandfather's Clock has been a household favourite for years and is still to be found in the Rotary Song Book.

Come Home, Father, however, was undoubtedly Mr. Work's star piece from the dramatic standpoint, and it has been the main-stay of the prohibitionists against every alluring stein song that ever emanated from a rathskeller. It is perhaps better known by ıs opening and most quotable line, "Father, dear father, come home with me now." If you are of a strongly emotional nature, you are warned against too great indulgence in this song:

Fa-ther, dear, fa-ther, come home with me now! The clock in the stee-ple strikes one.— You said you were com-ing right home from the shop, As soon as your day's work was done.— Our fire has gone out, our house is all dark, and moth-er's been watch-ing since tea,—— With poor broth-er Ben-ny so sick in her arms, And no one to help her but me.— Come home, come home, come home!— Please,— Fa-ther, dear Fa-ther, come home!— Hear the sweet voice of the child,[1] —— Which the night-winds re-peat as they roam! Oh, who could re-sist this most plain-tive of pray'rs? Please, Fa-ther, dear[2] Fa-ther, come home!

---

[1] At this point it was customary to insert a dash of coloratura, to represent the untrained but naturally flexible voice of the child.

[2] "Please" and "dear" may be sung as two-syllable words if desired. Do as you like about holding on to "father."

The story continues in the first person, and gradually approaches its dramatic climax in the following terms:

> Father, dear father, come home with me now!
>   The clock in the steeple strikes two;
> The night has grown colder, and Benny is worse - -
>   But he has been calling for you.
> Indeed he is worse—Ma says he will die—
>   Perhaps before morning shall dawn;
> And this is the message she sent me to bring—
>   "Come quickly, or he will be gone."
> Come home! come home! come home!
>   Please, father, dear father, come home.

> Father, dear father, come home with me now!
>   The clock in the steeple strikes three;
> The house is so lonely!—the hours are so long
>   For poor weeping mother and me.
> Yes, we are alone—poor Benny is dead,
>   And gone with the angels of light;
> And these were the very last words that he said—
>   "I want to kiss Papa good night."
> Come home! come home! come home!
>   Please, father, dear father, come home.

> P. S.   He came home.

ALLIE DARLING

H. P. Danks is best known as the composer of *Silver Threads among the Gold* (which is too accessible to require quoting here), but he wrote many other successful songs, some of them under assumed names. *Allie Darling* represents an early use of movie nomenclature, and the heroine belongs to that large family that includes various Nellies, Sallys, Jessies, Bessies, etc. The song would be worth remembering if only for its sturdy disregard of grammar in such phrases as, "Allie dear, for you and I." Credit for these effects, however, really belongs to J. T. Rutledge, the author of the words.[1]

---

[1] The influence of this usage is seen in a much later song, *Cheer Up, Mary*, which has the lines:

> Wedding bells will soon be ringing, ringing,
> And they'll ring for you and I.

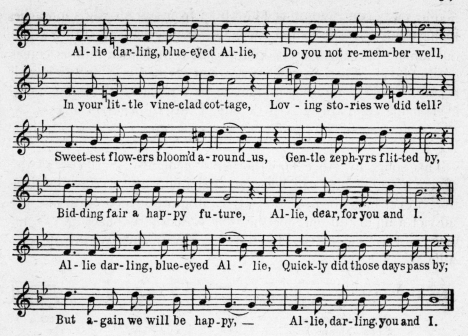

Al-lie dar-ling, blue-eyed Al-lie, Do you not re-mem-ber well,
In your lit-tle vine-clad cot-tage, Lov - ing sto-ries we did tell?
Sweet-est flow-ers bloom'd a - round_us, Gen-tle zeph-yrs flit-ted by,
Bid-ding fair a hap-py fu-ture, Al-lie, dear, for you and I.
Al - lie dar-ling, blue-eyed Al - lie, Quick-ly did those days pass by;
But a-gain we will be hap-py, — Al-lie, dar-ling, you and I.

Sunshine glisten'd on the waters
Of the little purling stream,
Birds were singing in the tree-tops,
Making life a pleasant dream;
And at night the silv'ry moonbeams
Floated on the calm, blue sky;
Stars were shining o'er us, darling,
Allie dear, o'er you and I.

'Tis a year since last we parted,
And I made you promise this:—
That you'd always love me, darling,—
Then I seal'd it with a kiss;
May our life be one of pleasure,
As it was in days gone by,—
May a sorrow ne'er o'ertake us,
Allie darling, you and I.

Silver Threads, by the way, is a far better song than is generally realized. Danks, who was a professional singer, knew how to write for the voice, and his technique of the legato line was copied by many composers, including himself.[1] In *Silver Threads*, however, he happened to strike a note of inevitability, which makes it stand out among all others of its kind. The song sold a million copies on its first publication, and later, when revived in connection with a play, it added another million to its circulation. Danks, however, made comparatively little out of this stupendous success.

LISTEN TO THE MOCKING BIRD

This song, by Alice Hawthorne, is generally sacrificed to the efforts of some bird-call whistler, and many are to-day unaware that it ever had words at all. It is still more surprising to find the subject a mournful one, for the tune is distinctly cheerful. Nominally, of course, Miss Hawthorne's Hally and Mr. Rutledge's Allie are twin sisters.

---

[1]Cf. *Allie Darling*, the melody of which might just as well be sung to *Silver Threads*.

Ah! well I yet remember, remember, remember,
 Ah! well I yet remember,
When we gather'd in the cotton side by side;
 'Twas in the mild September, September, September,
'Twas in the mild September,
 And the mocking bird was singing far and wide.   [*Chorus*]

When the charms of spring awaken, awaken, awaken,
 When the charms of spring awaken,
And the mocking bird is singing on the bough,
 I feel like one forsaken, forsaken, forsaken,
I feel like one forsaken,
 Since my Hally is no longer with me now.   [*Chorus*]

WE NEVER SPEAK AS WE PASS BY

Long before any one had thought of *A Bird in a Gilded Cage*, and all the other doleful commentaries of songdom's not angry but terribly hurt swains, the gentle art of infidelity had been jelled in a pleasing mould of melancholy through this anonymous but indubitably ancient song:[1]

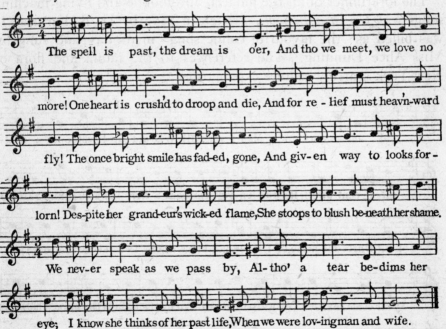

The spell is past, the dream is o'er, And tho we meet, we love no more! One heart is crush'd to droop and die, And for re-lief must heav'n-ward fly! The once bright smile has fad-ed, gone, And giv-en way to looks for-lorn! Des-pite her grand-eur's wick-ed flame, She stoops to blush be-neath her shame.

We nev-er speak as we pass by, Al-tho' a tear be-dims her eye; I know she thinks of her past life, When we were lov-ing man and wife.

[1] This, incidentally, is one of the earliest musical expressions of the "echo technique," immortalized in *How Dry I Am*, *And when I die*, *Say Au Revoir, but Not Good-bye*, and, most recently, *Sweet Adeline*. With a few changes in the notes, all of these songs can be sung in practically the same way.

In guileless youth I sought her side,
And she became my virtuous bride,
Our lot was peace, so fair, so bright,
One sunny day, no gloomy night;
No life on earth more pure than ours,
In that dear home, 'midst fields and flowers,
Until the tempter came to Nell,
It dazzled her, alas, she fell!

In gilded hall 'midst wealth she dwells,
How her heart aches, her sad face tells,
She fain would smile, seem bright and gay,
But conscience steals her peace away;
And when the flatterer casts aside
My fallen and dishonored bride,
I'll close her eyes, in death forgive,
And in my heart her name shall live.

UP IN A BALLOON

The forerunner of all the modern automobile and flying-machine songs was *Up in a Balloon*, written in 1869 by H. B. Farnie. It was billed as "the favourite comic song" in its day, and sung by Miss Alice Dunning. The references to the fauna and flora of New York scarcely require explanation.

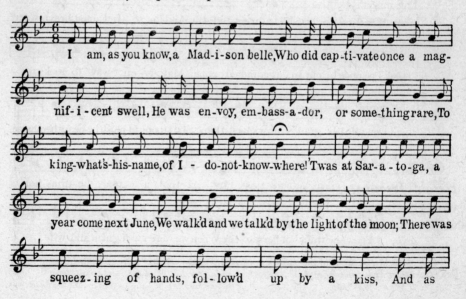

I am, as you know, a Mad-i-son belle, Who did cap-ti-vate once a mag-

nif-i-cent swell, He was en-voy, em-bass-a-dor, or some-thing rare, To

king-what's-his-name, of I - do-not-know-where! 'Twas at Sar-a-to-ga, a

year come next June, We walk'd and we talk'd by the light of the moon; There was

squeez-ing of hands, fol-low'd up by a kiss, And as

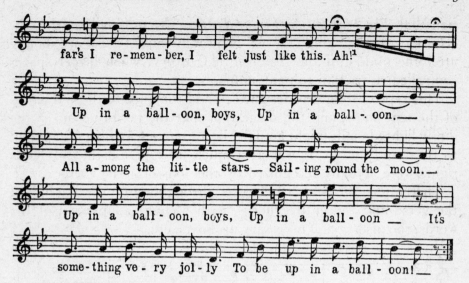

far's I re-mem-ber, I felt just like this. Ah!¹

Up in a ball-oon, boys, Up in a ball-. oon.___

All a-mong the lit-tle stars___ Sail-ing round the moon.___

Up in a ball-oon, boys, Up in a ball-oon ___ It's

some-thing ve-ry jol-ly To be up in a ball-oon!___

The wedding was fixed, the presents were bought,
And from Tiffany's jewelry was to be brought,
But alas, when the bill to my dear lover went,
By some misadventure he had not a cent!
My guardian, a broker away down in Wall,
Provided him plenty of funds at my call;
But when the old gentleman questioned where
His securities were, why, he answered "Up there!"—Ah! [Chorus]

The marriage guests came, I'd practised a tear,
I had got up a blush, and my veil was a dear,
And the parson was ready, likewise the champagne,
But ah! my false lover I ne'er saw again!
Instead of my darling, my hope and my joy,
There came to the altar a telegraph boy,
I saw that he knew, and I gasp'd out "O where
Is he gone?" and he pointed right up in the air! Ah!² [Chorus]

THE MAN ON THE FLYING TRAPEZE

So far as the editor knows, Harry Staton, of the New York
Herald Tribune, is the only man living who is thoroughly familiar
with this greatest of circus songs. He has not only contributed the
words and music from his active memory, but supplies the informa-

---

¹A florid cadenza was introduced here by Miss Dunning, to indicate agitation.

²Some years later, aërial transportation received more serious treatment in a song called
Don't Go up in That Balloon, Dad.

tion that *The Man on the Flying Trapeze* was originally in the repertoire of the "singing clowns," who went out of existence shortly after the middle of the Nineteenth Century, when bigger spaces compelled restriction to pantomime.

This type of song was designed to add romance to the acrobatics of the tent show, and the suggestion that the performer up in the dimly lighted vault might actually be a woman was most fascinating to rural audiences. It was at a much later period that woman's rights were actually recognized by the gods of aërial exercise.

The simple tune below can be used throughout, for the first half of the verse and the entire chorus, with a slight adaptation of the words, the insertion of necessary up-beats, etc.

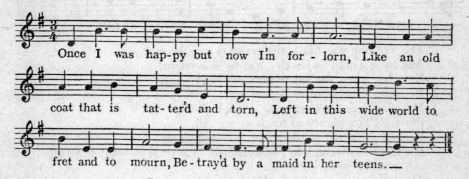

Once I was hap-py but now I'm for-lorn, Like an old coat that is tat-ter'd and torn, Left in this wide world to fret and to mourn, Be-tray'd by a maid in her teens.

The second half of the verse is as follows:

Now this girl that I lov'd she was hand-some, And I tried all I knew her to please, But I nev-er could please her one quar-ter so well Like that man on the fly-ing tra-peze.

Chorus: He flies through the air with the greatest of ease
This daring young man on the flying trapeze.
His movements are graceful, all girls he does please
And my love he's purloinéd away.

Now this young man by name was Señor Boni Slang
Tall, big and handsome, as well made as Chang.[1]
Where'er he appeared the hall loudly rang
With ovation from all people there.

He'd smile from the bar on the people below,
And one night he smiled on my love.
She winked back at him and she shouted bravo
As he hung by his nose up above. [*Chorus*]

Her father and mother were both on my side
And very hard tried to make her my own bride.
Her father he sighed and her mother she cried
To see her throw herself away.

'Twas all no avail, she went there every night
And threw him bouquets on the stage
Which caused her to meet him, how he ran me down
To tell it would take a whole page. [*Chorus*]

One night I, as usual, went to her dear home,
Found there her mother and father alone.
I asked for my love, and soon 'twas made known
To my horror that she'd run away.

She packed up her boxes and eloped in the night
With him with the greatest of ease.
From two stories high he had lowered her down
To the ground on his flying trapeze. [*Chorus*]

Some months after that I went into a hall,
To my surprise I found there on a wall
A bill in red letters which did my heart gall
That she was appearing with him.

He'd taught her gymnastics, and dressed her in tights
To help him to live at his ease.
He'd made her assume a masculine name
And now she goes on the trapeze.

Chorus: She floats through the air with the greatest of ease
You'd think her a man on the flying trapeze,
She does all the work while he takes his ease,
And that's what's become of my love.

MENAGERIE

The interest in the circus carried with it a number of early animal songs, of which the most popular was called *Menagerie*. It may be found in most of the old college song-books:

---

[1]This was the famous Chinese Giant.

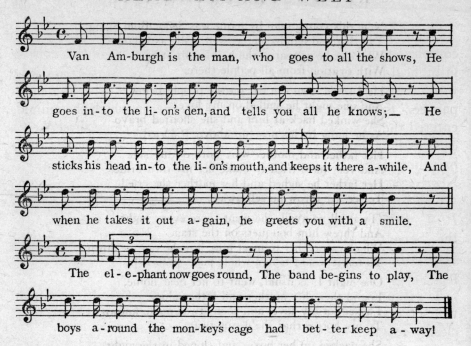

Van Am-burgh is the man, who goes to all the shows, He goes in-to the li-on's den, and tells you all he knows;— He sticks his head in-to the li-on's mouth, and keeps it there a-while, And when he takes it out a-gain, he greets you with a smile. The el-e-phant now goes round, The band be-gins to play, The boys a-round the mon-key's cage had bet-ter keep a-way!

First comes the African Polar Bear, oft called the Iceberg's daughter,
She's been known to eat three tubs of ice, then call for soda water;
She wades in the water up to her knees, not fearing any harm,
And you may grumble all you please, and she don't care a "darn."   [Chorus]

That Hyena in the next cage, most wonderful to relate,
Got awful hungry the other day, and ate up his female mate;
He's a very ferocious beast, don't go near him, little boys,
For when he's mad he shakes his tail, and makes this awful noise.   (Imitation of
    growling.)   [Chorus]

Next comes the Anaconda Boa Constrictor, oft called Anaconda for brevity,
He's noted the world throughout for his age and great longevity;
He can swallow himself, crawl through himself, and come out again with facility,
He can tie himself up with a double-bow-knot with his tail, and wink with the
    greatest agility.   [Chorus]

Next comes the Vulture, awful bird, from the mountain's highest tops,
He's been known to eat up little girls, and then to lick his chops;
Oh, the show it can't go on, there's too much noise and confusion,
Oh ladies, stop feeding those monkeys peanuts, it'll injure their constitution.
    [Chorus]

Noah's Ark provided a convenient background for the animal complex, and there were numerous ribald distortions of this episode in biblical history, from the sea chantey of *Old Man Noah*, who was "the original circus man" and "played poker with the chimpanzee," to the several versions of the manner in which the animals entered the Ark, "by twos," "two by two," "three by three," etc., each with an appropriate (or inappropriate) rhyme. (One of these has the refrain "There's one wide river," etc., and is actually a Negro spiritual in the process of elaboration.)

One of the most nonsensical of the circus and animal songs is *P. T. Barnum's Show*, whose performance in a drawing room of the 'Seventies always served to identify the town cut-up. This version is from the recollection of E. F. De Long, of Toledo (see p. 26).

The tune is not important, and that of *Menagerie* (see above) will serve as well as any other. In fact, the two songs seem to be closely related.

P. T. BARNUM'S SHOW

Good evening to you everyone.
    I brought the old banjo,
To tell you all what happened to me
    When I went to Barnum's Show.
I saw the leopard change his spots,
    Said one dog to another,
"Oh meet me, love, by the moonlight,
    And kiss me for your mother."

Chorus: If you want to have some fun,
    I will tell you where to go
To see the Lion stuffed with straw,
    At P. T. Barnum's Show.

The monkey and the elephant
    Were playing seven up,
The spider and the blue-tailed fly
    Were eating Kaiser's pup.
The kangaroo danced a polka
    With the baboon's little brother,
The skunk and the fat man got mixed up,
    So you couldn't tell which was 'tother. [*Chorus*]

Barnum and the happy family
  Went out on a drunk,
The alligator came rolling home,
  And rolled in the bull frog's bunk.
The camel called the kangaroo a liar,
  Said the baboon was a fool,
The mosquitoe got on his dignity,
  And pulverized the mule.   [*Chorus*]

It has been claimed that the oldest of all American animal songs is William Courtright's "Flew-y, Flew-y," whose words are sufficiently nonsensical to be preserved.

Elephant walked de rope—Flew-y, flew-y,
Elephant walked de rope—Flew-y an' a John.
Elephant walked de rope,
'Twas all full of grease and soap,
Wasn't that a fine walk?—Flew-y an' a John.

Chorus: Oh, Flew-y, flew-y, flew-y, flew-y,
Oh, Flew-y an' a John.
Oh, Flew-y an' flew-y,
Wasn't that a fine walk?—Flew-y an' a John.

Snail drew a rail—Flew-y, flew-y,
Snail drew a rail—Flew-y, flew-y.
Snail drew a rail,
Drew it with his tail,
Wasn't that a fine draw?—Flew-y an' a John.

Camel climbed a tree—Flew-y, flew-y,
Camel climbed a tree—Flew-y, flew-y.
Camel climbed a tree
For to catch the bumble bee.
Wasn't that a fine climb?—Flew-y an' a John.

Charles Taussig, New York lawyer and former Cornell athlete, still sings with gusto a famous animal song of the past. He insists upon dramatic facial expression, with a broad grin on the last line, and the voice rising to a falsetto squeak.

This is his version:

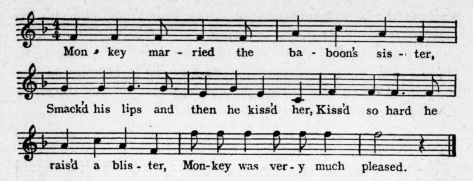

Mon - key mar - ried the ba - boon's sis - ter,

Smack'd his lips and then he kiss'd her, Kiss'd so hard he

rais'd a blis - ter, Mon-key was ver - y much pleased.

What do you think the bride was dressed in?
  White swiss dress and green glass breastpin,
  White kid shoes—were very interesting,[1]
  Monkey was very much pleased.

What do you think they had for supper?
  Black-eyed peas and bread and butter,
  Ducks in the duckhouse all a-flutter—
  Onions stewed and raw

Then there was the one about the "Animal Fair," with a chorus:

We went to the Animal Fair, The birds and the beasts were there,
The big baboon,[2] by the light of the moon, was combing his auburn hair.
The monkey he got drunk (he did)
He sat on the elephant's trunk (he did?)
The elephant sneezed and fell on his knees,
And that was the end of the monk, the monk, the monk, etc. [*ad infinitum.*]

O! FRED, TELL THEM TO STOP!

One of Tony Pastor's most popular comedy songs, and closely related to the prevalent enthusiasm for the circus, this boisterous ditty appeared strangely enough in a series of "English Ballads," published by S. T. Gordon & Son, by this time established on East Fourteenth Street. The motion of both the merry-go-round and the swing is in the music (by George Meen, who also did the words),

---

[1]The climax of a prize series of rhymes.
[2]Or "the old raccoon."

while in the background one can almost hear Van Amburgh's animals roaring.

Mr. Pastor always blared forth the word "Maria" in singing the chorus, and this is a necessary feature of the interpretation even to-day, with a falsetto quality, realistically feminine, on the phrase which gives the song its title.

No doubt you have heard of the Great Fan-cy Fair, That used to take place ev-'ry day,— Well I thought for a-muse-ment I'd take my girl there, To pass a dull hour— a - way,— We went in, you must know, and saw Bar-num's great show, Van Am-burgh's Me - nage - rie as well.— — There were round-a - bouts, swings and all kinds of things, For - get the day I nev- er shall.— Oh, Fred! tell them to stop! That was the cry of Ma - ri - a, But the more she said "Whoa", they said, "Let it go!" And the swing went a lit-tle bit high - er.

[*Spoken after first verse*]: Yes, when we got in the fair, my girl wanted to have a ride on one of the Swings. I said, "All right my darling," and we had a swing; but directly the swing went to and fro, she lustily called out: [*Chorus*]

The people that stood round of course they all laughed,
But I only said "Stop the swing!"
There were four or five others, in the "boats" beside us,
Saying "Master don't do such a thing!"
'Twas then that some roughs caught hold of the ropes,
Maria fell down on her knee,
And one of them said, "The young man's turning red,
But isn't he having a spree!" [*Chorus*]

They soon stopp'd the swing and Maria got out,
And quickly fell down on the floor,
They brought her some water, which soon brought her to,
This girl which I now do adore.
Should you ever go there, to the great Fancy Fair,
Friends, take advice whilst I sing
Of the great Round-a-bout, it's the best fun that's out,
And finish the day with a swing.

[*Spoken after third verse*]: Mark you, before you get into the "Swing boat," make a bargain with your young lady, not to call out: [*Chorus*]

THE MERMAID

Sailing parties with an urge for singing generally try this song after *My Bonnie Lies over the Ocean* and *Sailing, Sailing* have served their purpose. Few people know all the words to-day but *The Mermaid* still deserves a place of honour in any college group of the past century.

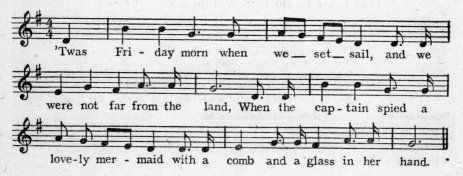

'Twas Fri-day morn when we set sail, and we were not far from the land, When the cap-tain spied a love-ly mer-maid with a comb and a glass in her hand.

Here is the chorus, as generally sung:[1]

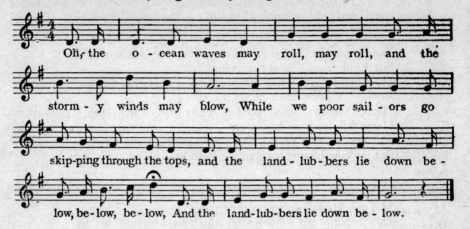

Oh, the o-cean waves may roll, may roll, and the storm-y winds may blow, While we poor sail-ors go skip-ping through the tops, and the land-lub-bers lie down be-low, be-low, be-low, And the land-lub-bers lie down be-low.

Then up spoke the captain of our gallant ship,
  And a well-spoken man was he,[2]
"I have married a wife in Salem town;
  And[3] to-night she a widow will be." [Chorus]

Then up spoke the boy of our gallant ship,
  And a well-spoken laddie was he,
"I've a father and mother in Boston city;
  And to-night they childless will be." [Chorus]

"Oh, the moon shines bright, and the stars give light;
  Oh, my mother'll be looking for me;
She may look, she may weep, she may look to the deep,
  She may look to the bottom of the sea." [Chorus]

Then up spoke the cook of our gallant ship,
  And a red hot cook was he,
"I care more for my kettles and my pots[4]
  Than I care for the bottom of the sea."[5] [Chorus]

---

[1]The original chorus ran:

> Oh, the stormy winds, how they blow, blow, blow,
> And the raging seas, how they go.
> While we poor sailors are climbing up aloft,
> And ye landlubbers lying down below, down below,
> And ye landlubbers lying down below.

[2]Sometimes revised: "And a right good captain was he."
[3]These "ands" were originally "buts."
[4]Sometimes sung: "My pottles and my kets."
[5]This stanza is a later addition.

Then three times round went our gallant ship,
  And three times round went she;
Then three times round went our gallant ship,[6]
  And she went to the bottom of the sea.   [*Chorus*]

'TWAS OFF THE BLUE CANARIES

This song, better known as *My Last Cigar*, has been popular in the colleges for the better part of a century.   The melody has been adopted by the University of Pennsylvania for an entirely serious Alma Mater anthem, with "O Pennsylvania" corresponding to the repeated lament of the chorus, "It was my last cigar."   (A parody, *My First Cigar*, of fairly obvious possibilities, was written by W. C. Rommel, the arch-wit of Princeton's class of '68.)

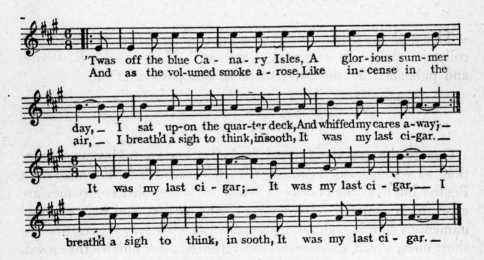

'Twas off the blue Ca - na - ry Isles, A glor-ious sum-mer
And as the vol-umed smoke a - rose, Like in-cense in the
day, — I sat up-on the quar-ter deck, And whiffed my cares a-way; —
air, — I breath'd a sigh to think, insooth, It was my last ci-gar. —
It was my last ci - gar; — It was my last ci - gar, — I
breath'd a sigh to think, in sooth, It was my last ci - gar. —

I leaned upon the quarter rail,
  And looked down in the sea,
E'en there the purple wreath of smoke
  Was curling gracefully;
Oh what had I at such a time
  To do with wasting care!
Alas, the trembling tear proclaimed
  It was my last cigar.

---

[6]Originally:

And the third time that our gallant ship went round,
She sank to the bottom of the sea.

I watched the ashes as it came
 Fast drawing toward the end;
I watched it as a friend would watch
 Beside a dying friend;
But still the flame crept slowly on;
 It vanished into air;
I threw it from me, spare the tale,—
 It was my last cigar.

I've seen the land of all I love
 Fade in the distance dim;
I've watched above the blighted heart,
 Where once proud hope hath been;
But I've never known a sorrow
 That could with that compare,
When off the blue Canaries,
 I smoked my last cigar.

This and the other college songs quoted here may be found in a collection called "Carmina Collegensia," edited by H. R. Waite, and published by the Oliver Ditson Company in 1868.

THE LONE FISH-BALL

One of the greatest favourites, better known to-day as a story than as a song, was *The Lone Fish-Ball*, subtitled "Founded on a Boston Fact (in the chorus of which all assembled companies are expected to unite)." It was one of the earliest and best of those immensely handy community songs in which a soloist presents two short lines, which are immediately repeated after him by the crowd.

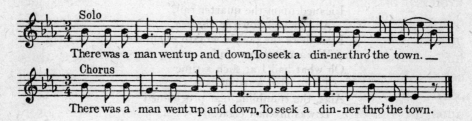

Solo
There was a man went up and down, To seek a dinner thro' the town. —

Chorus
There was a man went up and down, To seek a dinner thro' the town.

What wretch is he who wife forsakes,
Who best of jam and waffles makes!

He feels his cash to know his pence,
And finds he has but just six cents.

He finds at last a right cheap place,
And enters in with modest face.

The bill of fare he searches through,
To see what his six cents will do.

The cheapest viand of them all
Is "Twelve and a half cents for two Fish-ball."

The waiter he to him doth call,
And gently whispers—"One Fish-ball."

The waiter roars it through the hall,
The guests they start at "One Fish-ball!"

The guest then says, quite ill at ease,
"A piece of bread, sir, if you please."

The waiter roars it through the hall,
"We don't give bread with one Fish-ball!"

Moral

Who would have bread with his Fish-ball,
Must get it first, or not at all.

Who would Fish-ball with fixin's eat,
Must get some friend to stand a treat.

A curious footnote is appended in "Carmina Collegensia," telling an incident "singularly parallel," concerning "a certain learned Professor of New York: whose habit it became to frequent a place down town where buckwheat cakes were furnished." (These are now furnished up town also.) "Three buckwheat cakes were given for a sixpence. But the professorial appetite surpassed three cakes. Six cakes would have been given for 'twelve and a half cents,' but twelve and a half cents was a stretch of finances. Whereupon the Professor orders five buckwheats, which are sufficiently appeasing to his appetite, and for which he is content to pay tenpence. But the buckwheat people have no checks for tenpence—

their currency running in sixpences, shillings, and so on." Eventually the Professor becomes a notorious nuisance, "in fact becomes 'blown' at the establishment as the Five-buckwheat-man; and is one day resolutely informed that he must either go the six buckwheats or three buckwheats—or none at all. This upsets the Professor's pecuniary calculations, sours the buckwheats and his temper, and drives him away entirely." Truly a tragic tale!

THE DARK GIRL DRESSED IN BLUE

A ribald ditty among the college boys of the 'Sixties, celebrating the perils of that godless New York, and a forerunner of *The Bowery* and others of its kind, was *The Dark Girl Dressed in Blue*. Central Park is here the vicious circle, instead of the East Side, but the moral for provincial visitors is very much the same. Nothing gets a heartier laugh in the Sophisticated Metropolis today than the Poor Rube who falls for the most obvious chicanery. On the whole, the editor likes this one better than the newer versions. The melody is more original than the average, with a suggestion of actual folk-song and a touch of real individuality just before the typical refrain.

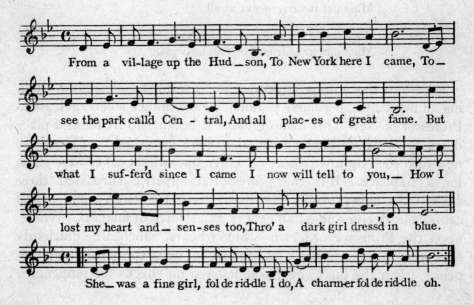

From a vil-lage up the Hud_son, To New York here I came, To_
see the park call'd Cen - tral, And all plac-es of great fame. But
what I suf-fer'd since I came I now will tell to you,_ How I
lost my heart and_ sen-ses too, Thro' a dark girl dress'd in blue.
She_ was a fine girl, fol de rid-dle I do, A charm-er fol de rid-dle oh.

'Twas on a Friday morning,
　　The first day of August;—
When of that day I ever think,
　　My heart feels ready to bust!
I jumped into a Broadway stage,
　　The Central Park going to,
On a seat by the right-hand side of the door,
　　Sat a dark girl dressed in blue.
　　　　She was, etc.

Now we hadn't gone very far,
　　When the lady looked so strange;
The driver knocked down for his fare,—
　　Says she, "I have no change;
I've only a ten dollar bill,
　　O dear, what shall I do?"
Said I, "Allow me to pay," "O, thank you, sir,"
　　Says the dark girl dressed in blue.
　　　　She was, etc.

We chatted and talked as we onward walked,
　　About one thing or the other;
She asked me, too, (O wasn't it kind?)
　　If I had a father or a mother.
Says I, "Yes, and a grandmother too;
　　But pray, miss, what are you?"
"O, I'm chief engineer in a milliner's shop,"
　　Says the dark girl dressed in blue.
　　　　She was, etc.

We walked about for an hour or two,
　　Through the park, both near and far;
Then to a large hotel we went—
　　I stepped up to the bar;
She slipped in my hand a ten dollar bill,
　　I said, "What are you going to do?"
"O, don't think it strange, I must have change,"
　　Said the dark girl dressed in blue.
　　　　She was, etc.

We had some slight refreshments,
　　And I handed out the bill;
The bar-keeper counted out the change,
　　And the bill dropped in the till;

'Twas in currency and silver change;
   There was a three-cent piece or two;
So I rolled it up, and gave it to
   The dark girl dressed in blue.
      She was, etc.

She thanked me, and said, "I must away;
   Farewell, till next we meet;
For on urgent business I must go
   To the store in Hudson street."
She quickly glided from my sight,
   And soon was lost to view;
I turned to leave—when by my side
   Stood a tall man dressed in blue!
      She was, etc.

This tall man said, "Excuse me, sir,
   I'm one of the 'special force';
That bill was bad—please come with me"—
   I had to go, of course.
Said I, "For a lady I obtained the change,"
   Says he, "Are you telling me true?
What's her name?"   Says I, "I don't know,
   She was a dark girl dressed in blue."
      She was, etc.

My story they believed—thought I was deceived,
   But said I must hand back the cash;
I thought it was a sin, as I gave her the tin—
   Away went ten dollars smash!
So, all young men, take my advice,
   Be careful what you do,
When you make the acquaintance of ladies strange,
   Especially a dark girl dressed in blue.
      She was, etc.

THE SON OF A GAMBOLIER

Below is probably the most popular of all those melodies that are at the service of the parodist, and the most adaptable to all occasions when special words of local significance are desired. The tune appears in most of the old college song-books, usually with the words of *The Son of a Gambolier*, which itself may be considered the most representative of the many vagabond songs of the world. The variants are numerous, both in text and in melody, and a good working version is all that can be attempted here. (The Irish origin is obvious.)

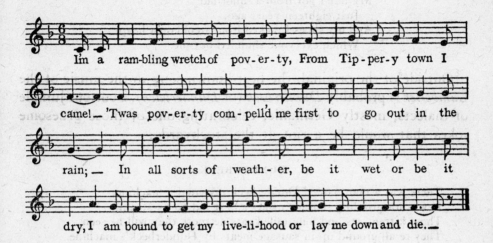

I'm a ram-bling wretch of pov-er-ty, From Tip-per-y town I came!— 'Twas pov-er-ty com-pell'd me first to go out in the rain; — In all sorts of weath-er, be it wet or be it dry, I am bound to get my live-li-hood or lay me down and die.—

Chorus:[1] Then combine your humble ditties,
　　　　As from tavern to tavern we steer,
　　　　Like ev'ry honest fellow,
　　　　I drinks my lager beer,
　　　　Like ev'ry jolly fellow,
　　　　I takes my whiskey clear,
　　　　I'm a rambling wretch of poverty,[2]
　　　　And the son of a gambolier.[3]

I once was tall and handsome,
　And was so very neat,
They thought I was too good to live,
　Most good enough to eat;
But now I'm old, my coat is torn,
　And poverty holds me fast,
And every girl turns up her nose,
　As I go wandering past.

---

[1]This chorus, to practically the same tune as the verses, is often made to begin:
　　　　Come join my humble ditty,
　　　　From Tippery town I steer.

[2]"Wretch" is commonly sung "rake."

[3]It is customary to repeat the last two lines of melody with the words: "I'm the son of a son of a son of a son of a son of a gambolier."

> I'm a rambling wretch of poverty,
>   From Tippery town I came,
> My coat I bought from an old Jew shop,
>   Way down in Maiden Lane;
> My hat I got from a sailor lad
>   Just eighteen years ago,
> And my shoes I picked from an old dust heap,
>   Which everyone shunned but me.

Outside of the original, the best-known song to the music of the *Gambolier* is probably *Dunderbeck* (or *Dunderbach*), a curious jumble of dialects, mostly Germanic, celebrating one of those gruesome jokes that would be a riot at the stockyards:

DUNDERBECK

There was a man named Dunderbeck invented a machine,
It was for grinding sausage meats and it did go by steam,
Those kitten cats and long-tailed rats no more they will be seen
They're all ground up in sausage meats by Dunderbeck's machine.

Chorus:
Oh, Dunderbeck, oh, Dunderbeck, you was so very mean![1]
Oh, don't you was so sorry you invented that machine?
Those kitten cats and long-tailed rats no more they will be seen,
They're all ground up in sausage meats by Dunderbeck's machine.

Now one fine day a boy came into Dunderbeck's store,
There was a pound of sausage meat a-lying on the floor,
And while he was a-waiting, he whistled up a tune,
The sausage meat began to yump and skip around the room.   [*Chorus*]

Now something was the matter, that machine he wouldn't go,
So Dunderbeck he scrambled inside to find him out, you know;
His wife she had the nightmare, she walked right in her sleep,
She grabbed the crank and gave it a yank, and Dunderbeck was meat.
                                                              [*Chorus*]

Malcolm ("Mike") Ross, who works for the Hotel Pennsylvania, New York, has brought the old *Gambolier* tune up to date, with a set of words that beautifully state the case for the rebel against morality. He divides credit, however, with Ralph ("Gee Gee") Albertson, who claims only a partial responsibility.

[1] Or "How could you be so mean?"

I have led a good life, full of peace and quiet,
But I shall have an old age steeped in rum and riot;
I have been a nice lad, careful of my morals—
I shall be a grandad full of vice and quarrels.

I have never cut throats—even when I've yearned to;
Never sung the queer songs that my fancy turned to.
I have been a good boy, cowed by smug conditions;
I have tied my real self tight in inhibitions.

I have been a sweet boy, wed to peace and study;
But I shall have an old age ribald, coarse and bloody—
With white hair and red face—full of hell and likker—
When I get a bad thought I shall let her flicker.

I shall quit the good life, full of peace and quiet,
And I shall be a Falstaff steeped in rum and riot—
I shall leave the straight path, which I've walked dejected;
I shall be an old bum—loved and unrespected.

There are many other sets of words to this universal tune, some of them of an unprintable vulgarity, but widely circulated, nevertheless, in the true folk-song style.

The conversational ballad type is preserved in a gently humorous poem, *The Young Oysterman*, by Oliver Wendell Holmes, originally having a tune of its own with a refrain:

With a Rook-chee-took, che-took-che-took-che,
Whack! Fol-lo! diddle-lol la day.

But it can be sung most effectively to the old *Gambolier* melody.

THE YOUNG OYSTERMAN

There was a tall young oysterman lived by the riverside,
His shop it was upon the bank, his boat was on the tide,
The daughter of a fisherman, that was so straight and slim,
Liv'd over on the other bank, right opposite to him.

It was the pensive oysterman, that saw a lovely maid,
Upon a moonlight evening, a-sitting in the shade;
He saw her wave her handkerchief, as much as if to say,
"I'm wide awake, young oysterman, and all the folks away."

Then up arose the oysterman, and to himself said he,
"I guess I'll leave the skiff at home, for fear the folks should see,
I read it in the story book, that, for to kiss his dear,
Leander swam the Hellespont, and I will swim this here."

And he has leaped into the waves, and crossed the shining stream,
And he has clambered up the bank, all in the moonlight gleam;
Oh, there were kisses sweet as dew, and words as soft as rain;
But they have heard her father's step, and in he leaps again!

Out spake the ancient fisherman—"Oh what was that, my daughter?"
"'Twas nothing but a pebble, sir, I threw into the water."
"And what is that, pray tell me, love, that paddles off so fast?"
"It's nothing but a porpoise, sir, that's been a-swimming past."

Out spoke the ancient fisherman, "Now bring me my harpoon!
I'll get into my fishing boat, and fix the fellow soon."
Down fell that pretty innocent, as falls a snow-white lamb,
Her hair drooped round her pallid cheeks, like sea-weed on a clam.

Alas for those two loving ones! She waked not from her swound.
And he was taken with the cramp, and in the waves was drowned;
But Fate has metamorphosed them, in pity of their woe,
And now they keep an oyster shop, for mermaids down below.

POLLY—WOLLY—DOODLE

This is the stock nonsense song of America, and about the only
one worth printing here. Most people know the tune but forget the
words:

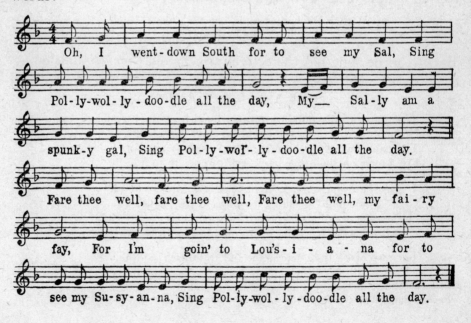

Oh, I went-down South for to see my Sal, Sing
Pol-ly-wol-ly-doo-dle all the day, My Sal-ly am a
spunk-y gal, Sing Pol-ly-wol-ly-doo-dle all the day.
Fare thee well, fare thee well, Fare thee well, my fai-ry
fay, For I'm goin' to Lou's-i-a-na for to
see my Su-sy-an-na, Sing Pol-ly-wol-ly-doo-dle all the day.

Oh, my Sal, she am a maiden fair,[1]
With curly eyes and laughing hair.

Oh, I came to a river, and I couldn't get across,
An' I jump'd upon a nigger, and I tho't he was a hoss.

Oh, a grass-hopper sittin' on a railroad track,
A-pickin' his teef wid a carpet tack.

Oh, I went to bed, but it wasn't no use,
My feet stuck out for a chicken roost.

Behind de barn, down on my knees,
I thought I heard that chicken sneeze.

He sneezed so hard wid de hoopin' cough,
He sneezed his head an' his tail right off.

BOHUNKUS

To the tune of *Auld Lang Syne*, the collegiate boys of the Nineteenth Century had a great time with this song:

There was a farmer had two sons,
    And these two sons were brothers;
Bohunkus was the name of one,
    Josephus was the other's.

Now, these two boys had suits of clothes,
    And they were made for Sunday;
Bohunkus wore his ev'ry day,
    Josephus his on Monday.

Now, these two boys to the theatre went,
    Whenever they saw fit;
Bohunkus in the gallery sat,
    Josephus in the pit.

Now, these two boys are dead and gone,
    Long may their ashes rest!
Bohunkus of the cholera died,
    Josephus by request.

---

[1]Repeat "Sing Polly-wolly-doodle all the day," after every line, and the chorus after every verse.

Now, these two boys their story told,
    And they did tell it well;
Bohunkus he to heaven went;
    Josephus went to——.[1]

Two more stand-bys of the old college song-books, and still popular when a crowd gets around the piano, are *There Is a Tavern in the Town* and *Clementine*.   Both melodies are quite familiar, but treacherous memories demand that the words be preserved, not necessarily in alcohol.   So here they are:

THERE IS A TAVERN IN THE TOWN

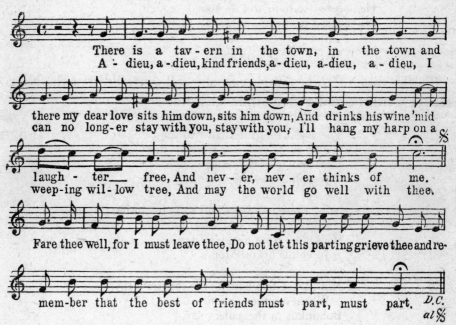

There is a tav-ern in the town, in   the town and
A - dieu, a -dieu, kind friends, a-dieu, a-dieu, a - dieu, I

there my dear love sits him down, sits him down, And drinks his wine 'mid
can no long-er stay with you, stay with you, I'll   hang my harp on a

laugh - ter__   free, And nev - er, nev - er thinks of   me.
weep-ing wil - low tree, And may the world go well   with thee.

Fare thee well, for I must leave thee, Do not let this parting grieve thee and re-

mem-ber that the best of friends must   part, must   part. *D.C.*
                                                                al %

He left me for a damsel dark, damsel dark,
Each Friday night they used to spark, used to spark,
And now my love, once true to me,
Takes that dark damsel on his knee. [*Refrain*]

---

[1] It was customary to sidestep the obvious rhyme. Sometimes it was merely swallowed up in a great shout of horror, or suggested by an awed silence. One book prints "Sing-Sing," in place of the telltale blank. "Now it can be told."

Oh! Dig my grave both wide and deep, wide and deep,
Put tombstones at my head and feet, head and feet,
And on my breast carve a turtle dove,
To signify I died of love. [*Refrain*]

CLEMENTINE

(Words and Music by Percy Montross)

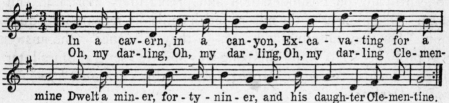

In a cav-ern, in a can-yon, Ex-ca-va-ting for a
Oh, my dar-ling, Oh, my dar-ling, Oh, my dar-ling Cle-men-

mine Dwelt a min-er, for-ty-nin-er, and his daugh-ter Cle-men-tine.
tine, You are lost and gone for-ev-er, Dref-ful sor-ry, Cle-men-tine.

Light she was, and like a fairy,
   And her shoes were number nine,
Herring-boxes, without topses,
   Sandals were for Clementine. [*Refrain*]

Drove she ducklings to the water,
   Ev'ry morning just at nine,
Hit her foot against a splinter,
   Fell into the foaming brine. [*Refrain*]

Ruby lips above the water,
   Blowing bubbles soft and fine,
Alas, for me! I was no swimmer,
   So I lost my Clementine. [*Refrain*]

In a churchyard, near the canyon,
   Where the myrtle doth entwine,
There grow roses, and other posies,
   Fertilized by Clementine. [*Refrain*]

Then the miner, forty-niner,
   Soon began to peak and pine,
Thought he "oughter jine" his daughter,
   Now he's with his Clementine. [*Refrain*]

In my dreams she still doth haunt me,
   Robed in garments soaked in brine,
Though in life I used to hug her,
   Now she's dead, I'll draw the line. [*Refrain*]

EARLY MISERIES

Songs of self-pity were exceedingly popular early in the Nineteenth Century, and these gradually developed a special school concentrating on misunderstood and prematurely moribund children. One pioneer of the misery fetish endlessly repeated the question, "Do they miss me at home, do they miss me?" (the answer was probably "No") and this song was imitated several times later. There was also *Nobody's Darling*, followed by *They Say I am Nobody's Darling*.

Put Me in My Little Bed was the seed for a whole harvest of baby songs, probably watered also by the gentle rain of Dickens's Little Nell and Mrs. Stowe's Little Eva. Thurland Chattaway wrote a popular plea for eliminating the colour line in *Little Black Me*, whose pathetic chorus started "Mama, are there any angels black like me?"

The gem of the children's crusade, however, was Ford and Bratton's *Only Me*, which guarantees tears of one kind or another any time it is properly sung. The first verse and chorus ran:

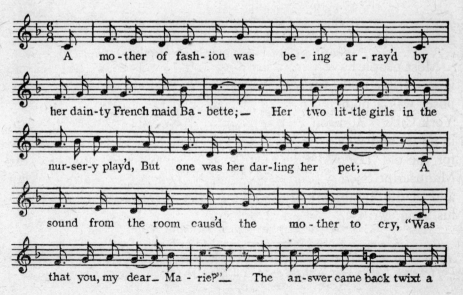

A mo-ther of fash-ion was be-ing ar-ray'd by her dain-ty French maid Ba-bette;— Her two lit-tle girls in the nur-ser-y play'd, But one was her dar-ling her pet;— A sound from the room caus'd the mo-ther to cry, "Was that you, my dear— Ma-rie?"— The an-swer came back twixt a

sob and a sigh, "No, ma - ma, it's on - ly me!"

On - ly me, on - ly me, sobb'd in a wear - y tone,

Wrung from an in - no - cent ba - by's heart, That felt so

much a - lone, One got the kiss - es and

kind - ly words, That was her pet, Ma - rie! One told her

trou - bles to bees and birds, That one was on - ly me!

(*Copyright, 1897, by M. Witmark & Sons. Used by permission.*)

The second verse, of course, lets the neglected child get even, by either dying or hovering on the brink of death, it doesn't matter which.[1]

ONLY A 'ITTLE DIRLY DIRL

Most people have a prejudice against baby-talk songs, but this one is so terrible that everyone is sure to like it. The author and composer was a highly respected character in the musical life of New York City, Addison Fletcher Andrews, a graduate of Dartmouth, in 1878, and a teacher in Columbia Grammar School. He wrote for the old *Tribune*, sang tenor in various churches, founded the Manuscript Society, and was assistant manager of Carnegie Hall and of the Symphony Orchestra of New York, 1891–92. Here is his song, with all the apostrophes:

---

[1] A song called *The House of Too Much Trouble* had a similar plot. Cf. also Chas. K. Harris's *Always in the Way*. The real classic of juvenile song literature, of course, is H. W. Petrie's *I Don't Want to Play in Your Yard*.

I love to sit up-on the floor, with nur-sey by my
side, Or munch a gweat big ap-ple core, My wock-ing horse ast-
wide.[1] I love to fool with' all my toys an' play at "hide-an'-
seet." But most of all I love the boys that live a-cwoss the
stweet.___ For I'm on-ly a 'it-tle dir-ly dirl, a
in-no-cent 'it-tle dir-ly dirl! With my dol-lies I
play, In the nur-sewy I stay, un-less I walk
out with Pa-pa;___ Yes, I'm on-ly a 'it-tle
dir-ly dirl, a good 'it-tle qui-et dir-ly
dirl! Ev-'wy hour in the day Twy-ing hard to o-
bey My dear-west, my sweet-est Ma-ma.___

I'm six years old two weeks ago, An' weigh just thirty-nine,
My hair is short but it will gwow, My eyes are large and fine,[2]
I wear the cutest 'ittle fwocks That ever you did see,
An' all the way from hat to socks, I'm sweet as sweet can be.

---

[1] For a girl of six, this is positively Shakespearean.
[2] Again the point of view suggests that of an adult.

Some day I'll be a gweat big dirl, An' have long dwesses too,
An' wear a necklace made of pearl, Just like my sister Lou,
I'll go to theatres, dances, balls, An' marwy some young man.
He'll take me to Niagawa Falls, Pwovidin' that he can.[3]

WHY DID THEY DIG MA'S GRAVE SO DEEP?

Here is a bit of macabre fancy, which would probably attract very little attention if it were not for its gorgeous title, which is also the last line of each stanza. J. P. Skelly, a prolific composer, was responsible for the music, and the words are by George Cooper. This song provided a splendid ensemble for the Twentieth Century "Fashion," and Deems Taylor has made a neat quartet arrangement, in which the melody of *Deep River* forms an admirable counterpoint to that of *Why Did They Dig Ma's Grave so Deep?*

Poor lit-tle Nel-lie is weep-ing to-night, Think-ing of days that were

full of de-light, Lone-ly she sits by the old kitch-en grate,

Sigh-ing for Moth-er, but now 'tis too late. Un-der the dais-ies now

cov-er'd with snow, Rests the fond moth-er, a - way from life's woe;

Nel-lie is left now to mur-mur and weep, Why did they dig Ma's grave so deep?

Why did they dig Ma's grave so deep, Down in the clay so deep?

Why did they leave me here to weep, Why did they dig Ma's grave so deep?

---

[3]This seems to be something of an anti-climax and rather disturbs the charmingly optimistic mood of the rest of the poem.

Only sweet mem'ries of gladness and love,
Come to the child of the dear one above,
Shadows are creeping around the lone room,
Early and late there's a feeling of gloom.
Out in the churchyard the wild breezes blow,
Seeming to echo her heart's grief and woe;
Softly she murmurs, while chills o'er her creep—
"Why did they dig Ma's grave so deep?"

Poor little Nellie in slumber's sweet rest,
Dreams all the night of the mother so blest,
Sees her again in a vision of light,
Praying, "God bless little Nellie to-night!"
Smiling upon her with glorified face,
Calling her home to that bright resting place;
Poor little Nellie oft sighs in her sleep—
"Why did they dig Ma's grave so deep?"

STROLLING ON THE BROOKLYN BRIDGE

The same combination of Skelly and Cooper produced a rival to *Walking Down Broadway*, called *Strolling on the Brooklyn Bridge*. This was written before Steve Brodie had made the bridge famous. It is an honest tribute to that thoroughfare's potentialities of sentiment, although a modern imagination may find it difficult to follow the course of events without getting mixed up in the traffic.

It's gay to ram-ble out at night with some nice girl so true; Then
in the love-ly pale moon light To care we bid a - dieu! The
fer-ry boat once took us home, My lit-tle girl and me; Now
o'er the Brooklyn Bridge we roam When moonlight tints the sea!

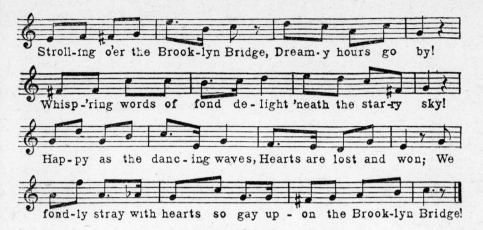

Stroll-ing o'er the Brook-lyn Bridge, Dream-y hours go by!

Whisp-'ring words of fond de-light 'neath the star-ry sky!

Hap-py as the danc-ing waves, Hearts are lost and won; We

fond-ly stray with hearts so gay up-on the Brook-lyn Bridge!

Some love to ramble in the park,
    When sunset hours are near;
Some love to linger, after dark,
    While stars are shining clear;
But give to me the pathway sweet
    Above the waters blue,
It's on the Brooklyn Bridge we meet,
    I and my darling true![1]

'Twas there our vows of love we told;
    'Twas there she gave to me
A promise, dearer far than gold,
    That ever true will be!
So, in the years that pass us by,
    I never shall forget
Those walks beneath the moonlit sky,
    Where first my love I met!

FLIRTING ON THE ICE

Isn't this just dandy? We simply must include it in our collection, if only for the sake of the picture, with its rakish petters, and the view of the Central Park Bridge and the old water tower in the distance. The words are by Arthur W. French, and the music by W. S. Mullaly, a famous minstrel of the '70's.

---

[1]This line should elect the author to the Lardnerian Order of the Pronoun. Probably her name was Sue too.

To Central Park one day,
    I took my love with me,
To pass the time away
    In skating merrily,
When on the gliding steel
    She whispered once or twice—
"Oh! George, my George, pray don't reveal
    Our flirting on the ice."

Chorus: For 'tis so entrancing,
    Better far than dancing,
    Softly smoothly gliding,
    Yes, pleasant words no chiding.
    Oh! so fascinating,
    Now what can equal skating?
    For nothing surely is so nice,
    When flirting on the ice.

I clasped her hand in mine,
    We talked of this and that,
While roguishly did shine
    Bright eyes 'neath jaunty hat,[1]
I hear her still repeat,
    These words of all so nice,
"Oh! George, my George, 'tis jolly sweet,
    This flirting on the ice."   [*Chorus*]

The sun went down the west,[2]
    The stars so brightly shone,
And wandering from the rest,
    I called her all my own,
She nestled to my side,
    And said "Oh ain't it nice?[3]
Yes! George, my George, you've won a bride,
    While flirting on the ice."   [*Chorus*]

(*Copyright, 1877, by D. S. Holmes*)

TWILIGHT IN THE PARK

This belongs with *Flirting on the Ice*, to complete the seasons in Central Park.   George Cooper wrote the words and W. H. Brockway the music, with the Ditsons the original publishers.   The same

[1]Well, look at the picture.
[2]As it does in all these nature songs.
[3]The English may be pardoned in her excitement.

old lake and bridge are visible, but "lover's lane" is now in "summer garb," and gondolas ply the waters, as never since.

'Twas on a summer's day,
 I met her all by chance;
Her smile was bright and gay,
 And loving was her glance!
We wandered in the "mall,"
 We strolled beside the "lake,"[1]
Her pretty hand so white and small
 Of course I chanced to take!
We talked about the swans and all the other birds,[2]
I thought I heard sweet music when I listened to her words![3]
She leaned upon my arm; the sun went down the west,
I tried in vain to whisper all the love within my breast!

Chorus: Twilight in the Park!
 Twilight in the Park!
  Cupid lingers there,
 And no one near to mark!
 Someone by your side,
  Happy as a lark!
 That's the time I love,
  Twilight in the Park!

She left me at the gate,
 And sweetly said good-bye;
I begged to know my fate,
 And half suppressed a sigh!
She said she'd come again,
 And named the time and place;
Her absence gave my heart such pain,
 For heaven shone in her face!
So every day I watched in love's delightful trance,
 And sure enough, we met again. She knew me at a glance!
'Twas love at sight, I said, and as the day grew dark,
I won her heart for evermore, at twilight in the Park! [*Chorus*]

Old-timers will remember one other park song that has served for innumerable dancing acts, both in its original form and as the background of parody. It was called *While Strolling through the*

---

[1]New Yorkers will recognize these spots with the mere lift of an eyebrow.

[2]This does not include the gondolas.

[3]Of course Goldman's band came much later.

Park, but many to-day would recognize the melody without knowing its title.

The Du Bell Twins introduced this song in 1880, getting it from the creative brain of Ed Haley, of the Haley Brothers. The traditional trick came after the double dance and break. At this point it was customary for the performers to take three steps solemnly to the left, raise the left hand toward the audience, and sing "Ah," pathetically, before repeating the first part of the music.

While stroll-ing thro' the park one day, In the mer-ry month of May, I was tak-en by sur-prise by a pair of ro-guish eyes, In a moment my poor heart was stole a-way. A smile was all she gave to me. (Dance and Break) Of course we were as hap-py as could be. (Dance and Break) Ah! I im-med-i-ate-ly rais'd my hat,— And fin-al-ly she re-mark'd: I nev-er shall for-get that love-ly af-ter-noon I met her at the foun-tain in the park![1]

A similar dance occurs in *The Big Sunflower*, written by Bobby

---

[1]These were the actual words, although they obviously make no sense. The absurdity was, of course, a deliberate burlesque of the sentimental park songs then in vogue.

Newcomb and sung by Billy Emerson, with an optimistic chorus, as follows:

> And I feel just as happy as a big sunflower,
> That nods and bends in the breezes.
> And my heart is light as the wind that blows
> The leaves from off the treeses.

Another elaborate dance, in triplets, occurred in *Marriage Bells*, which, it is said, was often played by its composer, on the musical glasses.

CHAMPAGNE CHARLIE

Up to 1895 or thereabouts, this was just the last word in devilishness. The original cover-design showed Charlie in blue-and-white striped trousers, a burnt-orange coat, gray suède gloves, and a silk hat, with a cigar tipped at a rakish angle between dangling whiskers that came down in points like the roots of a molar. In his right hand the hero held a stick, pointing at a champagne bottle in his left, from which the cork had popped, to form the dot on the i of his name above.

The piece could be had either as a song or as a gallop, and that placed it definitely among the rough and noisy dance tunes. The words were by G. Leybourne, the music by Alfred Lee, and the publisher was S. T. Gordon, of 706 Broadway, who evidently got it from England and adapted it to American conditions.

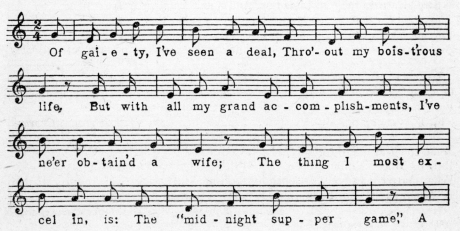

Of gai-e-ty, I've seen a deal, Thro'-out my bois-t'rous life, But with all my grand ac-com-plish-ments, I've ne'er ob-tain'd a wife; The thing I most ex-cel in, is: The "mid-night sup-per game," A

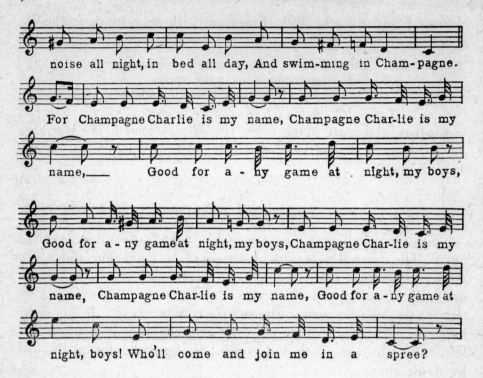

noise all night, in bed all day, And swim-ming in Cham-pagne.

For Champagne Charlie is my name, Champagne Char-lie is my

name,— Good for a-ny game at night, my boys,

Good for a-ny game at night, my boys, Champagne Char-lie is my

name, Champagne Char-lie is my name, Good for a-ny game at

night, boys! Who'll come and join me in a spree?

Mr. Leybourne did not lose much sleep over the creation of this rhymeless but quite explicit chorus. It's not so much the words, however, as the thought that is behind them. The song continues:

Where pleasures reign in cafés fine, And hotels grand I dwell,
The girls on seeing me exclaim, "Oh, what a Champagne swell!"
The notion 'tis of ev'ry one, That if 'twere not for my name,
And causing so much to be drunk, They'd never make Champagne. [*Chorus*]

The way I gain'd my title's By a fashion which I've got,
Of never letting others pay, However long's the shot,
For whoe'er drinks at my expense, Is treated all the same,
"Fifth Avenue" or "Bow'ry style," I make them take Champagne. [*Chorus*]

Some epicures like Burgundy, Hock, Claret and Moselle,[1]
But 'tis Moët's Vintage, only, Satisfies this Champagne swell!
What matter if to bed I go With head all muddled thick?
A "Champagne" in the morning Sets me "All right" very quick.

---

[1]These were all at one time well-known wines.

Perhaps you fancy what I say Is nothing more than chaff,
And only told, like other jokes, To merely raise a laugh!
But let me prove I'm not in jest; I'll stand a bottle o' "cham"[2]
For each man round! yes, that I will, And stand it like a lamb. [*Chorus*]

THE CAPTIVATING DUDE

Sardonic portraits of the lounge lizards of the 'Seventies failed
to dispel the type, but the red-blooded he-men of the day must have
enjoyed singing (with a lisp and a falsetto) such brutally accurate
descriptions as *The Captivating Dude* and *Lardy Dah*.

He walks along Fifth Avenue With steps of airy grace,
A look of limpid vacancy Upon his baby face;
His cane he poses in his hand With novel attitude,
His collar reaches to his ears, This captivating "dude"!

Chorus: Look at the "dude," Charming young dude,
Sweet-scented "baby," Saucy and rude,—
Collar so high, Pants to him glued,
Sweet captivating dude.

He ambles in his best make-up From noon till twilight gray;
You'll meet him anywhere in town Where fashion holds its sway;
He wears a rosebud in his breast And oft it is renewed,
He's sprinkled over with perfume, This captivating "dude"! [*Chorus*]

He's just too young to be a man, Too old to be a boy,
And when he meets a beauty's glance, His bosom heaves with joy,
He says, "Ah, there! you saucy thing!" He lisps a light "ta-ta,"
Oh! he's the very picture of A dandy "lah-de-da." [*Chorus*]

LARDY DAH

Let me introduce a fellah, Lardy dah! Lardy dah!
A fellah who's a swell, ah, Lardy, dah!
As he saunters through the street,
He is just too awful sweet;
To observe him is a treat, Lardy dah! Lardy dah!
Though of cash he lacks complete, Lardy dah!

---

[2]Short for "champagne." Unquestionably the song has lived up to its title.

Chorus: He wears a penny flower in his coat, Lardy dah!
   And a penny paper collar round his throat, Lardy dah!
  In his hand a penny stick, In his mouth a quill tooth-pick,
   Not a penny in his pocket, Lardy dah! Lardy dah!
  Not a penny in his pocket, Lardy dah!

  He is in a downtown office, Lardy dah! Lardy dah!
   And he's quite a city toff, is Lardy dah!
  He cuts a swell so fine,
   And he quite forgets to dine
  Unless he a friend can find, Lardy dah! Lardy dah!
   As to pay for hash and wine, Lardy dah! *[Chorus]*

  His shirt is very tricky, Lardy dah! Lardy dah!
   It's a pair of cuffs and dickey, Lardy dah!
  His boots are patent leather,
   But they never stand the weather,
  For they're paper glued together, Lardy dah! Lardy dah!
   Yes, they're paper stuck together, Lardy dah! *[Chorus]*

  His bogus diamonds glitter, Lardy dah! Lardy dah!
   But the girls all smile and titter, Lardy dah!
  If he stays out late at night, ah,
   And comes home rather tight, ah,
  And his luncheon's very light, ah, Lardy dah! Lardy dah!
   And this city swell so slight, ah, Lardy dah! *[Chorus]*

HAMLET, PRINCE OF DENMARK

To the intelligentsia, an illiterate account of any well-known classic has always been hugely amusing. Along with the eternally popular garbling of the Bible, the early Victorians heard such skits as the following on Hamlet, which occurs in college books of the time:

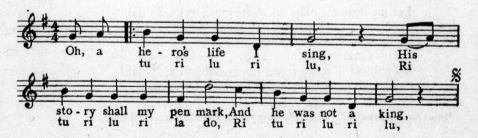

Oh, a he-ro's life I sing, His
tu ri lu ri lu, Ri

sto-ry shall my pen mark, And he was not a king,
tu ri lu ri la do, Ri tu ri lu ri lu,

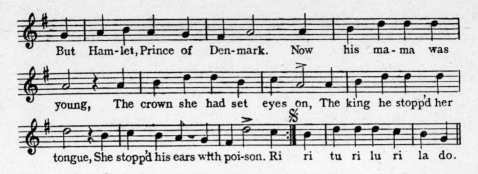

But Ham-let, Prince of Den-mark. Now his ma-ma was young, The crown she had set eyes on, The king he stopp'd her tongue, She stopp'd his ears with poi-son. Ri ri tu ri lu ri la do.

2. Now when she'd killed the king,
   She ogled much his brother;
   And having slain one spouse,
   She quickly took another;
   And this so soon did she,
   And was so great a sinner,
   That the funeral bakèd meats
   Set forth the wedding dinner.
       Ri tu ri lu, etc.

3. Now Hamlet sweet, her son,
   No bully or bravado,
   Of love felt hot the flame,
   And so went to Bernado;
   Oh sir! says one, we've seen
   A sight with monstrous sad eye;
   And this was nothing but
   The ghost of Hamlet's dad-i.
       Ri tu ri lu, etc.

4. Just at the time he spoke,
   It rose and said, "List, Hammy!
   Your mother was the ser-pi-ent
   That poisoned me, or d——n me;
   But now I'm gone below,
   All over sulph'rous flame, boy,
   That your dad should be on fire,
   You'll admit's a burning shame, boy."
       Ri tu ri lu, etc.

5. Just at the time he spoke,
   The morn was rising thro' dell;
   Up jumped a cock and cried,
   "A-cock-a-doo-del-doo-del";

"I'm now cock sure of going;
Preserve you from all evil;
You to your mother walk,
And I'll walk to the d——l."
    Ri tu ri lu, etc.

6. Now Hamlet loved a maid,
    And calumny had passed her;
    She never had been mar-ri-ed,
    'Cause nobody had asked her.
    But madness seized her brain,
    The poor cham-*ber*-lain's daughter,—
    She jumped into a pond,
    And went to heaven by water.
        Ri tu ri lu, etc.

7. But enough of that; they had a play;
    They had a play, and sham'd it;
    With Clau-di-us for au-di-ence,
    And he got up and d——d it.
    He said he'd see no more,
    And felt a wondrous dizz'ness;
    And so for candles called,
    To make light of the business.
        Ri tu ri lu, etc.

8. A fencing match they had;
    The queen drank while they try to;
    Says she, "Oh king, I'm killed";
    Says Laertes, "So am I too";
    "And so am I," says Ham;
    "What! can all these things so true be!"
    "What, are you dead?" says the king,—
    "Yes, sir; and so shall you be."
        Ri tu ri lu, etc.

9. So Hamlet stabbed his liege,
    Then fell on Ophy's brother;
    And then the Danish court
    All tumbled one on t'other.
    To celebrate their deeds,
    Which are from no false sham let,
    Every village small,
    Henceforth was called a "Hamlet."
        Ri tu ri lu, etc.

THE ELOPEMENT

T. B. Prendergast, of Campbell's Minstrels, the Julian Eltinge of his day, used to present this song in his most popular female impersonation. The words are by J. S. Freligh, the music by J. H. Ross, and the original copyright by Balmer & Weber. The editor discovered it in an old volume belonging (by inheritance) to Miss Martha Kroupa, his efficient secretary, whose significant aid in compiling "Read 'Em and Weep" is hereby gratefully acknowledged.

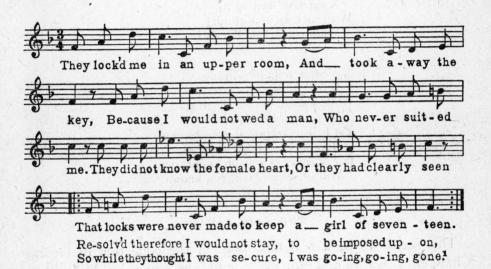

They lock'd me in an up-per room, And took a-way the key, Be-cause I would not wed a man, Who nev-er suit-ed me. They did not know the female heart, Or they had clearly seen That locks were never made to keep a girl of seven-teen.

Re-solv'd therefore I would not stay, to be imposed up-on,
So while they thought I was se-cure, I was go-ing, go-ing, gone![1]

They had a gilded cage in view,
  And thought the bird secure,[2]
Surrounded by the guards of power,
  And ev'ry artful lure:
They never thought of counterplots
  In anyone like me,
And little knew what I would do
  For Love and Liberty.[3]

---

[1] It's a small world, after all, according to the Herpicide People.

[2] This also sounds familiar.

[3] Perhaps taking a crack at the current political songs, which all glorified some such combination.

They wanted me to marry rich,
　　Unmindful of the means,
To couple me with wealth and age,
　　While I was in my teens;
But being "otherwise engaged,"
　　No coaxing could prevail,
And I preferred to please myself,
　　And would not be for sale.

The night was dark, the window raised,
　　How could I answer no?
When that might be my only chance
　　And Charley teased me so.
A railroad station being near,
　　A carriage waiting by,
With such an opportunity,
　　What could I do but fly?

Not being fond of solitude,
　　It had for me no charms,
While I could knot a silken cord
　　To reach a lover's arms;
Yet half regretting thus to leave,
　　'Twould disappoint them so,
But schemes of watchful guardians
　　Will sometimes fail, you know.[4]

THE ERIE CANAL

This seems to be a real folk-song, in the collection of George Chappell ("Captain Traprock"), and also sung by Mike Ross (see p.80). The "fifteen miles" line evidently refers to the average day's run on the old canal, although some versions have it "sixteen years." Two verses and a chorus give the spirit of the song:

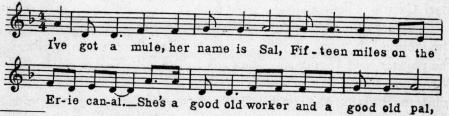

I've got a mule, her name is Sal, Fif-teen miles on the Er-ie can-al.—She's a good old worker and a good old pal,

[4]You haven't said the half of it, dearie.

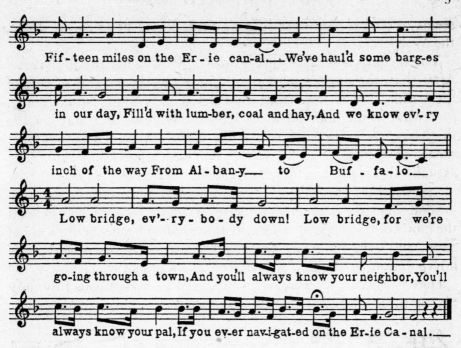

Fif-teen miles on the Er-ie can-al.—We've haul'd some barg-es in our day, Fill'd with lum-ber, coal and hay, And we know ev'-ry inch of the way From Al-ban-y— to Buf-fa-lo.—

Low bridge, ev'-ry-bo-dy down! Low bridge, for we're go-ing through a town, And you'll always know your neighbor, You'll always know your pal, If you ev-er nav-i-gat-ed on the Er-ie Ca-nal.—

Get up there, Sal, we passed that lock.
We'll make Rome 'fore six o'clock,
One more trip and back we'll go
From Albany to Buffalo. [*Chorus*]

WILLIE, THE WEEPER

This is one of the few American songs that can stand with *Frankie and Johnnie* as epic material of the underworld. The editor got it from Joe Cook, that unique comedian, who sang it for him with a guitar accompaniment in his dressing room at the Earl Carroll Theatre.

There are other versions, one in the repertoire of Roderick White, the violinist (brother of Stewart Edward, the novelist, and Gilbert, the painter, and Harwood, the poet), but this one seems authentic. Mr. Cook found it many years ago at the Alamo, a disreputable joint in Buffalo, and it was even then considered an old song. (Montague Glass claims to know *Willie, the Weeper*, but his version seems to consist mainly of "Ta da ya ta da da ya ta da da Willie, the Weeper.")

The melody is written down here only as it fits the first verse. After that, the singer has to adapt himself to the natural accents of the words. It is important to keep a slow syncopation going, somewhat in the manner of the later *Casey Jones* and that low-life rhapsody, *Ashes to Ashes* or the *Hesitatin' Blues*. Brian Hooker speaks of emphasizing this syncopation with an occasional sniff, but actually this is not a sniffing song, as its text clearly refers to those merry Oriental pastimes of smoking opium and injecting cocaine.

Sometimes the dream of Willie, the Weeper, is carried far beyond the limits of this version, as, for instance, when he meets the King of Siam, and wins his money at poker. But there is a suspicion of interpolation in these ultra-modern examples of vice.

Here is Mr. Cook's version, which need be accompanied by only two or three chords at the piano, or with a guitar or ukulele:

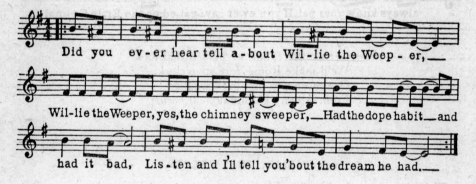

Did you ev-er hear tell a-bout Wil-lie the Weep-er,—
Wil-lie the Weeper, yes, the chimney sweeper,—Had the dope habit—and
had it bad, Lis-ten and I'll tell you 'bout the dream he had.—

'Round the lay-out a couple of hop-fiends lay,
Listen and I'll tell you what they had to say,
Tales of money they were going to make,
And faro banks that they were going to break.

I heard one big hop-fiend say,
"Grand scheme I got on to-day,
Got an interest in a silver-mine,
Left to me by a friend of mine.

"Got a ruby-bush, a diamond-mine.
An emerald-tree, a sapphire-vine,

Hundreds of railroads that run for miles,
A thousand dollars' worth of coke[1] stacked up in piles."

They started off in a Pullman car,
Did not get so very far.
In their minds they had the railroad cinched;
They woke up in the morning, found the joint was pinched.

They marched them off to the station-house,
Meek as a lamb, quiet as a mouse;
"What's the charge?" the judge then said,
"Hittin' up the hypo,"[2] and the fiend dropped dead.

"But I beg to differ," said the other smoker,
"The cop is kidding, he's quite a joker,
I'm the King, the land of poppies is my home."
"Twenty-three,"[3] said the judge. "Show the King his throne."

They went to the land called Kankantee,
Bought a million cans of hop and had a jubilee,
Visited the neighbors for miles around,
Presented the King with a bottle of Crown.[4]

He went to Monte Carlo where he played roulette,
Won every penny and he never lost a bet.
Played all night till the bank went broke,
Laid himself down and took another smoke.

This is the tale of Willie, the Weeper,
Willie, the Weeper, yes, the chimney-sweeper,
Fell asleep on his hall-room cot,
Dreamed he had a million dollars' worth of hop.[5]

---

[1] This has nothing to do with coal. Snow would be a better guess.
[2] This does not mean that the victim was subject to hypochondria.
[3] This expression proves the antiquity of the song.
[4] A famous brand of "hop," according to Mr. Cook.
[5] This line should be sung with considerable slowing of the time.

At the very end of the song, this refrain is introduced, with appropriate blue harmonies:

But in the morn-ing,—where am I at?___ I thought that I was___ in my sweet ba-by's flat,___ But in the morn-ing ___ I'm right in line,___ Mister Hop Sing Toy you're no friend of mine.___

CASEY JONES

Here is the greatest of all railroad songs. It has often been imitated, but never successfully.

Written by two actual railroad men, T. Lawrence Seibert and Eddie Newton, it breathes the nonchalant recklessness of the old-time engineer.[1] (The name itself has been bequeathed to one of our modern aëronauts and some say that its original owner was from Kansas City, and hence called "K. C.")

Casey Jones runs most of the way in true ballad style, and it is only the unexpected close that puts it in the comedy class. A seeming imitation, by Henry Whitter, called *The Wreck on the Southern Old 97*, not only dwells abominably on too civilized details ("It was on this grade when he lost his air-brakes," "He was going down grade making ninety miles an hour," etc.), but ends in a moralizing strain quite at variance with the care-free solution of the original:

> So come on, you ladies, you must take warning
> From this time now and on,
> Never speak harsh words to your true loving husband,
> He may leave you and never return.

Away with such milk-and-water dilutions, and have at you with the epic of the steel rails!

---

[1] The Leightons, who wrote *Steamboat Bill*, which is the *Casey Jones* of water travel, are sometimes credited with the authorship of the railroad classic as well, but Bert Leighton, surviving member of the team, disclaims the honor and states he got it from Newton and Seibert. The song is reprinted on the following page by permission of Shapiro, Bernstein & Co., owners. Copyright, 1909, by Newton & Seibert. Copyright renewed.

Casey Jones should be sung in a strongly syncopated fashion, letting the words themselves create the logical accents. You will find they can be fitted to the general outline of the melody as given below. Two or three chords are enough for an accompaniment, with the rhythm strongly emphasized throughout. It has always been customary to sing the chorus with everyone shouting the name of the hero, while a solo voice takes the intervening lines.[2]

---

[2]The railroad terms in this ballad scarcely need explaining. The rounders who are asked to listen to the story are obviously the men in the round-house, while the six eight wheeler is the type of engine that Casey drove.

Put in your water and shovel in your coal,
Put your head out the window, watch them drivers roll,
I'll run her till she leaves the rail,
'Cause I'm eight hour late with that western mail.
He looked at his watch and his watch was slow,
He looked at the water and the water was low,
He turned to the Fireman and he said,
"We're going to reach Frisco but we'll all be dead."

Chorus: Casey Jones!   Going to reach Frisco,
          Casey Jones!   But we'll all be dead.
          Casey Jones!   Going to reach Frisco.
          We're going to reach Frisco, but we'll all be dead.

Casey pulled up that Reno hill,[3]
He tooted for the crossing with an awful shrill,
The switchmen knew by the engine's moan
That the man at the throttle was Casey Jones.
He pulled up within two miles of the place,
Number Four stared him right in the face,
Turned to the Fireman, said, "Boy, you'd better jump,
'Cause there's two locomotives that's a-going to bump."[4]

Chorus: Casey Jones!   Two locomotives!
          Casey Jones!   That's a-going to bump!
          Casey Jones!   Two locomotives!
          There's two locomotives that's a-going to bump.

Casey said just before he died,
"There's two more roads that I'd like to ride."
Fireman said, "What could that be?"
"The Southern Pacific and the Santa Fe."[5]
Mrs. Jones sat on her bed a-sighing,
Just received a message that Casey was dying,
Said "Go to bed, children, and hush your crying,
'Cause you got another papa on the Salt Lake Line."[6]

---

[3]As so many others, before and since!

[4]Just why this wreck was necessary has never been made clear. Unquestionably, however, there was a wreck, and it was a good one.

[5]In making this choice, Casey must have had in mind chiefly the requirements of the ballad-writer as to rhyme and rhythm.

[6]It seems there were two Irishmen!

Chorus: [7]Casey Jones! Got another papa!
Casey Jones! On that Salt Lake Line!
Casey Jones! Got another Papa!
And you've got another Papa on that Salt Lake Line.[8]

---

[7]The original version inserts "Mrs." at this point, with a fine feeling for accuracy. But this detail was seldom observed in the actual singing of the song.

[8]This, of course, is the reverse of the usual Salt Lake procedure. Scholars have been puzzled by the problem of whether Mrs. Jones was merely fortifying the spirit of the children with a most excusable falsehood, or whether she actually had an emergency engineer in the background. Probably it is best to consider it an ordinary case of polyandry and let it go at that.

THE EASTERN TRAIN

This song, also known as *The Pullman Train*, is said to have originated in Scotland, but is now thoroughly Americanized. There are many versions, although everyone agrees as to the main facts of the charmingly romantic story.

The editor first heard it in the late 'Nineties (when it was already an old song) while camping in the Thousand Islands, where it was part of the extensive repertoire of the Macgurn sisters, now living in Detroit. (Olive is an excellent kindergarten teacher, and Bessie married James Devoe, the local concert manager.) Father Macgurn would always say, after his daughters had finished their popular duet, "That's the cutest song I ever heard!"

Try it on a really rough party some time.

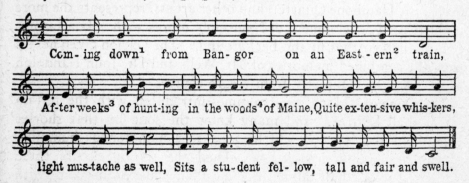

Com- ing down[1] from Ban- gor on an East - ern[2] train,

Af-ter weeks[3] of hunt-ing in the woods[4] of Maine, Quite ex-ten-sive whis-kers,

light mus-tache as well, Sits a stu- dent fel- low, tall and fair and swell.

---

[1]Or "up" as the case may be.

[2]This became eventually a "Pullman train," although that type of car would have made the story impossible.

[3]The Macgurns sang "six months' shooting."

[4]Or "wilds."

Empty seat behind him, no one at his side,
  As into a pleasant station the Eastern train doth glide.
Enter agèd couple, take the hindmost seat,
  Enter lovely maiden, bewitching and petite.

Blushingly she murmurs, "Is this seat engaged?"
  See the elder couple properly enraged!
Student, quite delighted, sees her ticket "through,"
  Thinks him of the tunnel and knows what he will do.

So they sit and chatter, as the cinders fly,
  Until the student fellow gets one into his eye.
Maiden, sympathetic, turns her quick about
  And says, "Sir, if you please, may I try to take it out?"

Soon the student fellow feels her tender touch,
  And hears her softly murmur, "Does it hurt you much?"
Whiz! bang! boom!   Into the tunnel quite,
  And all is glorious darkness, as black as Egypt's night.

Out into the daylight glides the Eastern train,
  Student's hair is ruffled just the slightest grain,
Maiden is all blushes,[5] and there next appeared
  A tiny little ear-ring, caught in student's beard!

MONA (YOU SHALL BE FREE)

This curious song, a favourite in the repertoire of John Barnes
Wells, the Hambone Quartet, and other artists, represents the more
sophisticated development of Negro folk-music, with only a suggestion of the spiritual in the background.   The version given here is
from the combined memories of Mr. Wells and Dr. John Randolph
Page, who got it directly from Negro sources.

The name of "Mona" is sometimes introduced with the refrain
"You shall be free," and many know the song by that shorter
title.   The first part should be sung to a monotonous humming
accompaniment, in minor key.   Then the refrain occurs three
times, the soloist half talking the questions and exclamations, with
the quartet or chorus breaking in, "You shall be free," in harmony,
and everybody coming strong on "When de good Lord sets you

---

[5]This and the preceding line are sometimes sung "Student's beaver's ruffled, etc.   Maiden's hair is
rumpled."

free," at the end of each stanza. Endless topical verses can be and have been added to the original text:

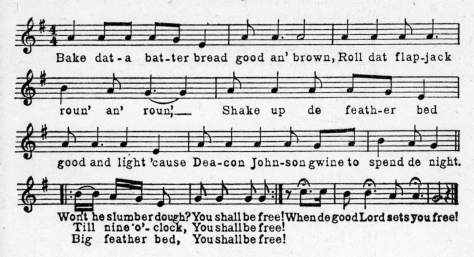

Bake dat-a bat-ter bread good an' brown, Roll dat flap-jack roun' an' roun', ___ Shake up de feath-er bed good and light 'cause Dea-con John-son gwine to spend de night.

Won't he slumber dough? You shall be free! When de good Lord sets you free!
Till nine 'o'- clock, You shall be free!
Big feather bed, You shall be free!

Some folks say dat a dummy can't run,
Jes' let me tell you what de dummy done done,
She left Memphis at half past one,
An' she run into Natchez by de settin' o' de sun.
Wan't she movin', dough'?—You shall be free!
Sho' turnin' a wheel!—You shall be free!
Easin' right along!—You shall be free!
When de good Lord sets you free!

I got on de dummy an' I didn't had no fare,
Corndoctor ask me what I doin' dar.
Took me by de arm an' led me to de door,
Told me not to git on dat dummy no more.
Wan't he mean to me?—You, etc.
I'se ridin', dough!—You, etc.
Wan't payin' nothin'!—You, etc.
When de good, etc.

I got a girl, she work so hard,
Work over yonder in de white folks' yard.
She kill a turkey and she save me de tail,[1]
Thinks I'm a-workin' but I layin' in jail!

---

[1]Another version is:

She kill a turkey and she save me de stuffin',
She think I'm workin', but I ain't doin' nothin'.

Ain't I foolin' her?—You, etc.
Eatin' turkey, dough!—You, etc.
Lots o' stuffin' in it!—You, etc.
When de good, etc.

Went down town to roll some bones,
Wid a great big nigger by de name o' Jones,
He roll seven 'leven and sure as you're alive,
I came back at him wid a three, four, five!
Wan't he shootin' 'em?—You, etc.
Sho' rollin' em!—You, etc.
Little josie too!—You, etc.
When de good, etc.

Peter Jackson so slick and black,
Hit Frank Slavin de finishin' crack.[2]
Jumped on de dummy and he pulled de cord,
You'd a thought dat nigger was an English Lord.
Hard hittin' nigger!—You, etc.
Big black nigger!—You, etc.
Great bruiser!—You, etc.
When de good, etc.

Great big nigger was lyin' side a log,
Wid his finger on de trigger, an eye on de hog;
Boy pulled de trigger an' de gun went crack,
Hog fell down right flat o' his back.
Good pork chops!—You, etc.
Jowl and gravy too!—You, etc.
Hawg Haslets!—you, etc.
When de good, etc.

---

[2] A reference to one of the historic fights of the great Negro champion.   Jack Johnson was introduced into later verses.

THE VOGUE OF HARRIGAN AND HART

HARRIGAN AND HART are familiar names to most Americans, but actually little is known to-day about this famous team. They were perhaps the most gifted comedians of the 'Seventies, and their vogue lasted until the death of Tony Hart in 1891.

The Harrigan and Hart partnership was formed in 1871, but before this Hart had appeared as "Master Anthony Cannon," singing ballads with various minstrel companies. He has been called "probably the best 'genteel wench' that ever trod the boards."

Ned Harrigan was known as "Pete" in their black-face act, but they also specialized in Irish songs, and later worked up the elaborate musical comedies which travelled all over America. Harrigan himself wrote the words of all their most famous songs, and the music was written by David Braham, orchestra leader of "The Mr. Josh Hart Combination."

One of their greatest hits was *The Mulligan Guard*, presented at the Chicago Academy of Music in 1873, and this satire practically disrupted the amateur military organizations which had flourished since the Civil War, chiefly for political and convivial reasons. The tune, however, achieved honest popularity and actually figures in Kipling's "Kim," as the favourite band piece of the English soldiers in India.

Here is the ringing chorus of that martial air:

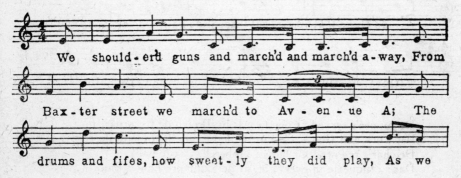

We should-er'd guns and march'd and march'd a-way, From
Bax-ter street we march'd to Av-en-ue A; The
drums and fifes, how sweet-ly they did play, As we

march'd, march'd, march'd in   the   Mul - li - gan   Guard. __

THE SKIDMORE FANCY BALL

Several years later, the *Mulligan Guard* idea had developed into a complete musical play, and this contained a similar travesty on a coloured company, *The Skidmore Fancy Ball:*

Oh, here we go so nobly, Oh! de Colored Belvidere,
A number one, we carry a gun.   We beat de Fusileers.—
You talk about your dancers, when we hear de cornet call,
We wing and wing, de dust we sling, at de Skidmore Fancy Ball.
Now right and lef, just hold your bref,
We're bon ton darkies all,
De fat and lean get in and scream at de Skidmore Fancy Ball.

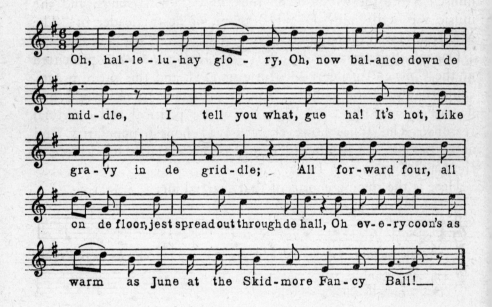

Oh, hal-le-lu-hay glo - ry, Oh, now bal-ance down de mid - dle, I tell you what, gue ha! It's hot, Like gra-vy in de grid-dle; All for-ward four, all on de floor, jest spread out through de hall, Oh ev-e-ry coon's as warm as June at the Skid-more Fan-cy Ball! __

De supper's served at one G. M. by Brown de Catoroar,
Fat Turk and Goose, oh, cut me loose, just lem me in de door.
De char's reserved for ladies' umberellas in de hall,
Dar's ettiquette in every set, at de Skidmore Fancy Ball.

Den hands around, keep off de ground,
We're bon ton darkies all,
Get in and sail, do hold your grail at de Skidmore Fancy Ball.

Oh every hat dat dey get at, dis Colored Coterie,
Will cost a half, you needn't laugh, Oh help de Millishee.—
We're gwine down to Newport just next Summer in de Fall,
So follow suit and contribute, at de Skidmore Fancy Ball.
Oh waltz away, and mazurka,
We're bon ton darkies all,
Sweet Caledone, it gives a tone to de Skidmore Fancy Ball.

There was also a "Mulligan Guard Chowder," which contained
another Skidmore song, *The Skids Are out To-day*, and "The Mulligan Guard Nominee," with *The Skidmore Masquerade*, not to speak
of "The Mulligan Guards' Christmas" with *The Pitcher of Beer*,
and "The Mulligan Guard Picnic" with *Mary Kelly's Beau* and
Sandy-Haired Mary in Our Area.

THE BABIES ON OUR BLOCK

In the original "Mulligan Guard Ball" was also one of the best-
loved Harrigan and Hart songs, *The Babies on Our Block*, a forerunner of *The Sidewalks of New York* and all its tribe, with some
actual quotations from old Irish tunes.   Here are the words:

If you want for information, Or in need of merriment,
Come over with me socially To Murphy's tenement;
He owns a row of houses In the First Ward, near the dock,
Where Ireland's represented By the Babies on our Block.
There's the Phalens and the Whalens From the Sweet Dunochadee,
They are sitting on the railings With their children on their knee,
All gossiping and talking With their neighbors in a flock,
Singing, "Little Sally Waters," With the Babies on our Block.
Oh, Little Sally Waters, Sitting in the sun,
A-crying and weeping for a young man;
Oh, rise, Sally, rise, Wipe your eye out with your frock;
That's sung by the Babies a-living on our Block.

Of a warm day in the summer, When the breeze blows off the sea
A hundred thousand children Lay on the Battery;
They come from Murphy's building, Oh, their noise would stop a clock!
Oh there's no perambulatory, With the Babies on our Block.

There's the Clearys and the Learys From the sweet Black Water side,
They are laying on the Battery And they're gazing at the tide;
All royal blood and noble, All of Dan O'Connell's stock,
Singing, "Gravel, Greeny Gravel," With the Babies on our Block.
Oh, Gravel, Greeny Gravel, How green the grasses grow,
For all the pretty fair young maidens that I see;
Oh, "Green Gravel Green," Wipe your eye out with your frock;
That's sung by the Babies a-living on our Block.

It's good morning to you, landlord; Come, now, how are you to-day?
When Patrick Murphy, Esquire, Comes down the alley way,
With his shiny silken beaver, He's as solid as a rock,
The envy of the neighbors' boys A-living off our Block.
There's the Brannons and the Gannons, Far-down and Connaught men,
Quite easy with the shovel And so handy with the pen;
All neighborly and friendly, With relations by the block,
Singing "Little Sally Waters," With the Babies on our Block.
Oh, Little Sally Waters, Sitting in the sun,
A-crying and weeping for a young man,
Oh, rise, Sally, rise, Wipe your eye out with your frock;
That's sung by the Babies a-living on our Block.

THE WIDOW NOLAN'S GOAT

The huge success of the Harrigan and Hart plays must have been due entirely to their honest comedy values, for certainly the titles were not particularly attractive. One was called simply "Investigation," and in another, "Squatter Sovereignty," appeared that popular Irish song, *The Widow Nolan's Goat.*

Oh, I'm a lone widdy, I meself and my daughter,
    We live in a house where there's welcome galore;
My husband he formally[1] carried up mortar
    From the ground to the third or fourth floor;
When he died he will'd over the land and the shanty;
    His pipe and his stick, and his frieze overcoat;
The pig and the goslins, the chickens so banty,
    And his favorite pet, oh, my buck Billy Goat.

---

[1]Probably no reference to his manners was intended.

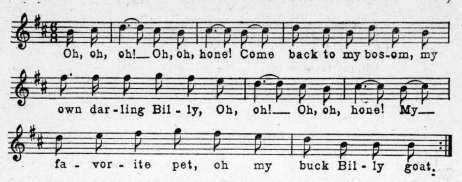

Oh, oh, oh!__Oh, oh, hone! Come back to my bos-om, my own dar-ling Bil - ly, Oh, oh!__ Oh, oh, hone! My__ fa - vor - ite pet, oh my buck Bil - ly goat.

Wid horses he slept ev'ry night in the stable;
　　He'd rise in the morn at the break o' the day;
When breakfast was ready he'd come to the table;
　　Sure I never could drive him away;
He could butt down a fence, oh, so gentle and aisy;
　　He'd stand near the pond for to see the ducks float;
He'd climb o'er the hills, sure he never was lazy;
　　My own favorite pet, oh, my buck Billy Goat.

His whiskers were long like the Wandering Jew man;
　　He ate up old hoop-skirts, newspapers and rags;
When a kid he belonged to young Mary Ann Doolan;
　　He would skip and sleep out on the flags;
'Twas a blast from the quarry struck him on the shoulder
　　The morning my husband went out for to vote;
He laid sick abed from the fall of the boulder
　　Did my favorite pet, oh, my buck Billy Goat.

He'd fight like a trooper; his horns were like sabers;
　　He'd bate all the goats for so many miles round;
Sure he'd butt at a stranger *butt* never a neighbor;
　　Sure they could not take him to the pound;
Oh, his right name was Willy, but I called him Billy;
　　He was my companion; on him sure I'd dote;
So fond of sunflowers and daffydowndillies
　　Was my favorite pet, oh, my buck Billy Goat.

His white hairs were silken, they hung long and drooping;
　　He traveled some time with Mike Reagan's Big Nan;
If a child in the neighborhood took on a crooping,
　　He'd halt and he'd gaze like a man;

All the dogs and the cats sure they'd never come near him;
Wid his horns he would buck them a terrible smote;
The long years and days it took me for to rear him,
Oh, my favorite pet, oh, my buck Billy Goat!

(Copyright, 1881, by Wm. A. Pond & Co. Used by permission.)

PADDY DUFFY'S CART

In the same play was *Paddy Duffy's Cart*, similar in spirit to *The Babies on Our Block* and still remembered as a typical New York song:

The ma-ny hap-py eve-nings I spent when but a lad On Pad-dy Duf-fy's lum-ber cart, quite safe a-way from dad; It stood down on the cor-ner, near the old lamp-light. You should see the con-gre-ga-tion there on ev-'ry summer night Oh, there was Tom-my Dob-son, now a sen-a-tor; Bil-ly Flyn and John-ny Glyn, oh, they were kill'd in war: All mer-ry boy-ish com-rades, re-col-lec-tions bring, All seat-ed there in Duf-fy's cart on sum-mer nights to sing!

---

[1]After the first and third verses it was customary to insert the old chorus of *Twinkling Stars Are Laughing, Love*, in close harmony.

We'd gather in the evening, all honest working boys,
And get on Paddy Duffy's cart for no one marr'd our joys;
All seated in the moonlight, laughing 'mid its rays,
Oh, I love to talk of old New York, and of my boyish days.

Chorus: Oh, there was Henry Gleason, now a millionaire;
Curly Rob and Whitey Bob, they're living on the air:
All merry boyish comrades, etc.[2]

Oh, a merry little maiden, so nobby, neat and coy,
A-smiling up at Duffy's cart upon her sweetheart boy:
It made a jealous feeling, a quiet piece of chaff;
But all in play it died away and ended with a laugh.

Chorus: Oh, there was Larry Thomson, dear old chum of mine:
Lemmy Freer and Sandy Greer, they died in forty-nine;
All merry boyish comrades, etc.

MAJOR GILFEATHER

Finally, in 1881, Harrigan and Hart produced, in "The Major,"
one of the classics of eccentric character music, *Major Gilfeather*,
the perfect revelation of the mid-Victorian fop who had previously
been only haltingly lampooned in such songs as *The Captivating
Dude, Lardy Dah*, etc. Ladies and gentlemen, meet the Major:

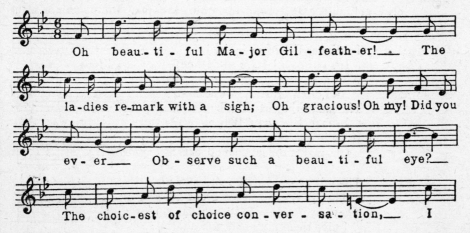

Oh beau-ti-ful Ma-jor Gil-feath-er! The
la-dies re-mark with a sigh; Oh gracious! Oh my! Did you
ev-er Ob-serve such a beau-ti-ful eye?
The choic-est of choice con-ver-sa-tion, I

---

[2]After the second verse the procedure was varied by having Harrigan sing "Little Frank" four
times, with Hart interrupting: "What's the matter?" "She chews tobacco," and "Umberellas,"
concluding, "She's the daintiest darling of all."

give to the la-dies, oh dear! In ho-tel, in par-lor, or sta-tion,— Oh, this is the lan-guage I hear: Oh, how is the Ma-jor Gil-feath-er?— I'm a lit-tle bit un-der the weather!— It's smil-ing-ly then I'd en-dea-vor— To bor-row a five, do you see?— Oh, take it and keep it for-ev-er! — My friend-ship for you can-not sev-er,— For you are so roy-al-ly clev-er!— Oh, mean-ing the Ma-jor, that's me!—

To dinner I'm often invited,
  It's out of my style to decline;
With rapture and joy I'm delighted,
  And often prostrated with wine;
The ladies they say I'm bewitching,
  In fact, I'm a real Belvedere![1]
In ballroom, in parlor, or kitchen,
  Oh, this is the language I hear:— [Chorus]

The tailors and barbers all know me,
  They're envious of my great success,
They say, "Come and pay what you owe me!"
  I give them my name and address;

[1] A favourite word with Ned Harrigan. He must have read about that statue of Apollo some-where, and the idea haunted him.

I leave them to mingle with fashion,
   Their voices grate hard on my ear;
When hungry, and needing a ration,
   Oh, this is the language I hear:— [*Chorus*]

THE FREE-LUNCH CADETS

John Philip Sousa composed this song, words and music, when he was playing the violin in a Philadelphia theatre orchestra in 1877. It is, therefore, as a museum piece that it is included here. The terrific drawing on the title page gives a vivid impression of the old free-lunch days, and the words of the chorus suggest that one could gather a fairly good meal for the price of a glass of beer in the Quaker City. The music has a touch of the later Sousa in its sturdy six-eight march time.

This unique piece in the creative repertoire of the march king was introduced by Griffin and Rice, a song and dance team, probably at Dumont's or Carncrosses' Minstrel Show, but its reputation may well have been entirely local.[1]

The general description seems to fit the rathskeller that used to be on the corner of Broad St. and Penn Square, opposite the Public Buildings.

We circumnavigate the town for every free-lunch bar;
We go from east to west and back, and travel wide and far.
We sometimes get into a bar where lunch has just run out,
And all that's left to feed upon is the smell of sauerkraut.
We're always near to take a beer when we've a chance to beat,
And while we're here we'll tell our fare, and what we get to eat.

Chorus:
Oh, sauerkraut and barley soup, and corn beef by the slice,
Red herrings sprinkled o'er with salt, we tell you they are nice:
Limburger cheese and mushroom pie, and hot corn by the ear—
You wouldn't have, you couldn't get, a better bill of fare. [*Repeat*]

---

[1] The only existing copy of *The Free-Lunch Cadets*, so far as the editor knows, is in the possession of William J. McKenna, to whom Mr. Sousa himself has admitted his responsibility for the song. (See the identification of McKenna with *Has anybody here seen Kelly?* p. 237)

We're drumming up recruits to-day, to join our noble band;
We want you all to sign your name, and lend a helping hand.
You'll have a free and easy time—it's jolly, you can bet,
To be a member and be called a prime free-lunch cadet.
We're always near to take a beer when we've a chance to beat,
And while we're here we'll tell our fare, and what we get to eat. [*Chorus*]

SOMEBODY'S GRANDPA

A quotation from the New York *Tribune*, in the late 'Seventies, gives the background to this song:

A little girl in town recently saw an old drunken man lying on a doorstep, the perspiration pouring off his face, and a crowd of children preparing to make fun of him. She took up her little apron and wiped his face, and then looked up so pitifully to the rest and said, "Oh, don't hurt him! He's somebody's grandpa!"

This neat bit of reporting was turned by C. F. Wood into a song that ranks close to *Come Home, Father* in the annals of the American struggle for temperance. It appeared in the Saalfield "Olio" of 1880.

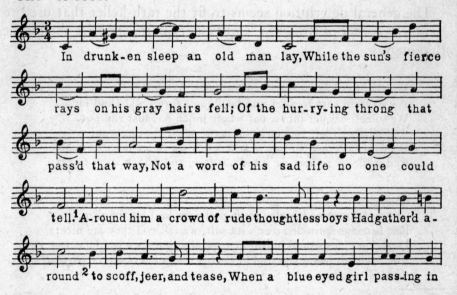

In drunk-en sleep an old man lay, While the sun's fierce rays on his gray hairs fell; Of the hur-ry-ing throng that pass'd that way, Not a word of his sad life no one could tell.[1] A-round him a crowd of rude thoughtless boys Had gather'd a-round[2] to scoff, jeer, and tease, When a blue eyed girl pass-ing in

---

[1] Mr. Wood believes that one good negative deserves another.
[2] He will make this picture clear if he has to repeat every word.

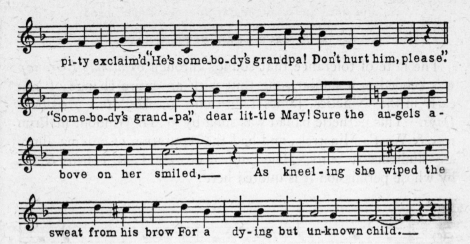

pi-ty exclaim'd, "He's some-bo-dy's grandpa! Don't hurt him, please."

"Some-bo-dy's grand-pa," dear lit-tle May! Sure the an-gels a-

bove on her smiled,— As kneel-ing she wiped the

sweat from his brow For a dy-ing but un-known child.—

This immediately complicates the plot and introduces an element of suspense.   Now go on with the story.

In the stifling glare of an attic room
    Where the sun poured in with its fiercest power,
A pale little blue-eyed girl suffering lay,
    Watching and waiting from hour to hour.
"I'm hungry," she whispers, "starving for bread,"
    Then silently turns to the wall and cries.
"Why don't grandpa come?   Perhaps he is dead!"
    'Tis well she can't see where his gray head lies. [*Chorus*]

The cool dew of night falls soft on his brow,
    And on his bruised face; he awakes with a cry,
"Am I mad, am I dreaming?   Oh! where am I now?
    O Bessie, my darling, I've left you to die!"
With trembling steps he reaches his home,
    And kneels by her bed in sad despair,
While pale Bessie murmurs her last earthly words,
    "I knew you'd come, Grandpa, God answered my prayer." [*Chorus*]

O dear little children! never forget,
    Though the life of a man may be sinful and wild,
There still may be hearts to whom he is dear;
    He may yet own the love of an innocent child.
He's somebody's grandpa, brother, or friend,
    You may bruise some child's heart when you laugh at and tease,[3]
So silence the jest, hear May's pleading words,
    "He's somebody's grandpa!   Don't hurt him, please." [*Chorus*]

---

[3]Him or it, as the case may be.

SHE MAY HAVE SEEN BETTER DAYS

The note of tolerance that sounds through *Somebody's Grandpa* was echoed in a similar song (but with an entire change of cast) early in the 'Nineties, James Thornton's *She May Have Seen Better Days*. This pathetic ballad was sung by W. H. Windom in Primrose & West's Minstrels, and had the reputation of moving almost any audience to tears. The publishers were T. B. Harms & Co., by whose permission it is quoted here:

While stroll-ing a - long with the ci-ty's vast throng, On a night that was bit-ter-ly cold,___ I no-ticed a crowd who were laugh-ing a-loud At some-thing they chanc'd to be-hold.___ I stopped for to see what the ob-ject could be, And there, on a door-step, lay___ A wom-an in tears, from the crowd's an-gry jeers, And then I heard some-bo-dy say:___ She may have seen bet-ter days,___ When she was in her prime;___

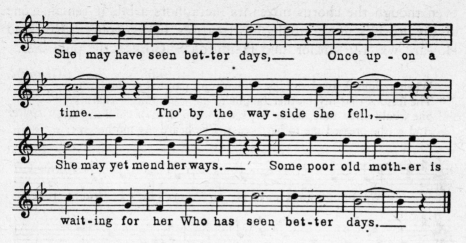

She may have seen bet-ter days,___ Once up - on a time.___ Tho' by the way-side she fell,___ She may yet mend her ways.___ Some poor old moth-er is wait-ing for her Who has seen bet-ter days.___

"If we could but tell why the poor creature fell,
   Perhaps we'd be not so severe;
If the truth were but known of this outcast alone,
   Mayhap we would all shed a tear.
She was once someone's joy, cast aside like a toy,
   Abandoned, forsaken, unknown."
Every man standing by had a tear in his eye,
   For some had a daughter at home.   [*Chorus*]

The crowd went away, but I longer did stay;
   For from her I was loth to depart.
I knew by her moan, as she sat there alone,
   That something was breaking her heart.
She told me her life, she was once a good wife,
   Respected and honored by all;
Her husband had fled ere they were wed,
   And tears down her cheeks sadly fall.   [*Chorus*]

YOU NEVER MISS THE WATER TILL THE WELL RUNS DRY

Let it never be said that the ribald songs of the Nineteenth Century outnumbered the virtuous. For every lyric endorsement of intemperance, there was an equally powerful presentation of the advantages of the restrained and moral life.

"Adage songs" were very popular as stimulators of uplift, and the best known of the lot was *You Never Miss the Water Till the Well Runs Dry*. There is practically no answer to this argument, and even though the chorus mixes its metaphors a bit, it remains one of the world's most intelligible treatises on economy. Rowland Howard was the author, and Hamilton S. Gordon the publisher.

When a child, I lived at Lincoln, with my parents at the farm,
The lessons that my mother taught to me were quite a charm;
She would often take me on her knee, when tired of childish play,
And as she pressed me to her breast, I've heard my mother say:

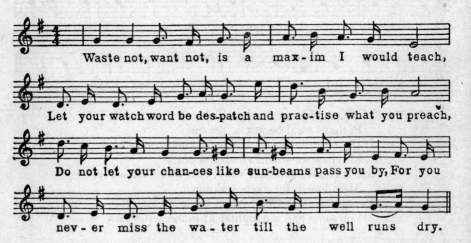

Waste not, want not, is a max-im I would teach,
Let your watchword be des-patch and prac-tise what you preach,
Do not let your chan-ces like sun-beams pass you by, For you
nev - er miss the wa - ter till the well runs dry.

As years rolled on, I grew to be a mischief-making boy!
Destruction seemed my only sport, it was my only joy;
And well do I remember, when oft-times well chastised,
How father sat beside me, then, and thus has me advised: [Chorus]

When I arrived at manhood, I embarked in public life,
And found it was a rugged road, bestrewn with care and strife;
I speculated foolishly, my losses were severe;
But still a tiny little voice kept whispering in my ear: [Chorus]

Then I studied strict economy, and found to my surprise,
My funds, instead of sinking, very quickly then did rise;
I grasped each chance, and always "struck the iron while 'twas hot,"
I seized my opportunities, and never once forgot: [Chorus]

I'm married now, and happy, I've a charming little wife,
We live in peace and harmony, devoid of care and strife;
Fortune smiles upon us, we have little children three;
The lesson that I teach them as they prattle round my knee: [Chorus]

ALWAYS TAKE MOTHER'S ADVICE

Another splendidly moral song of the 'Eighties was called *Always Take Mother's Advice*, words and music by Jennie Lindsay. It was a true prophecy of "Mother's Day," and anxiously endorsed that filial affection which means so much to the florists, stationers, and candy-manufacturers to-day.

Honor your mother, so dear,
    You'll ne'er know her worth 'till she's gone;
Respect her grey hair while she's here,
    You'll be sad when she leaves you alone.
On earth you will ne'er have another,
    In this weary world there's no other,
And God only gives you one mother!
So cherish and love her most dear.

ABDUL ABULBUL AMIR

One of the first non-stop songs to run between New York and San Francisco was *Abdul Abulbul Amir*. It was the direct and only tangible result of the Crimean War, and started a school of Oriental atmosphere whose influence is still felt in American song literature![1]

Nobody knows to-day just how many verses of *Abdul* are in existence. The version given below is essentially that of the recently published "Book of Navy Songs," collected and edited by the Trident Literary Society of the U. S. Naval Academy at Annapolis, but there are many variants. Even the name of the hero can be spelled several different ways, and that of his rival alternates (in the middle) between "Petrusky" and "Skavinsky."

The authentic melody is given below, with an additional tune at the end, which some may find easier, and which has frequently been used, particularly in the colleges. (*Abdul* sings quite well also to Sullivan's *Little Buttercup* waltz, from "Pinafore.")

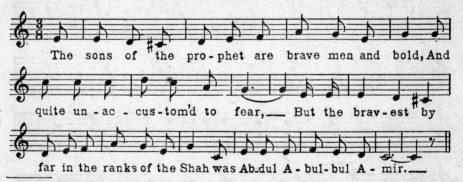

The sons of the pro-phet are brave men and bold, And quite un-ac-cus-tom'd to fear,— But the brav-est by far in the ranks of the Shah was Ab-dul A-bul-bul A-mir.—

[1] A splendid modern example is *The Sultan's Wives*, by Bobby Edwards, also in the repertoire of F. Gregory Hartswick. (See p. 223.)

2. If you wanted a man to encourage the van
        Or harass the foe from the rear,
    Storm fort or redoubt, you had only to shout
        For Abdul Abulbul Amir.

3. Now the heroes were plenty and well known to fame
        In the troops that were led by the Czar,
    And the bravest of these was a man by the name
        Of Ivan Skavinsky[2] Skavar.

4. He could imitate Irving, play poker and pool,
        And strum on the Spanish guitar,
    In fact quite the cream of the Muscovite team
        Was Ivan Skavinsky Skavar.

5. One day this bold Russian had shouldered his gun,
        And donned his most truculent sneer,
    Downtown he did go, where he trod on the toe
        Of Abdul Abulbul Amir.[3]

6. "Young man," quoth Abdul, "has life grown so dull[4]
        That you wish to end your career?
    Vile infidel, know, you have trod on the toe
        Of Abdul Abulbul Amir."

7. Said Ivan, "My friend, your remarks in the end
        Will avail you but little, I fear,
    For you ne'er will survive to repeat them alive,
        Mr. Abdul Abulbul Amir.[5]

8. "So take your last look at sunshine and brook,
        And send your regrets to the Czar—
    For by this I imply, you are going to die,
        Count Ivan Skavinsky Skavar!"

9. Then this bold Mameluke drew his trusty skibouk,
        With a cry of "Allah Akbar,"
    And with murderous intent he ferociously went
        For Ivan Skavinsky Skavar.

---

[2] Or "Petrusky."

[3] A variant is:

> And assumed his most truculent leer,
> At the rise of the sun, he just happened to run
> Into Abdul Abulbul Amir.

[4] Some sing "Said Abdul, 'Young man, has your life been so dull?" and insert a "now" into the next line.

[5] This stanza is not in the navy version, but it ought to be.

10. They parried and thrust, they sidestepped and cussed,
    Of blood they spilled a great part;
  The philologist blokes, who seldom crack jokes,
    Say that hash was first made on that spot.

11. They fought all that night 'neath the pale yellow moon
    The din, it was heard from afar,
  And huge multitudes came, so great was the fame,
    Of Abdul and Ivan Skavar.

12. As Abdul's long knife was extracting the life,
    In fact he was shouting "Huzzah,"
  He felt himself struck by that wily Calmuck,
    Count Ivan Skavinsky Skavar.

13. The Sultan drove by in his red-breasted fly,
    Expecting the victor to cheer,
  But he only drew nigh to hear the last sigh
    Of Abdul Abulbul Amir.

14. Czar Petrovitch too, in his spectacles blue,
    Rode up in his new crested car.
  He arrived just in time to exchange a last line
    With Ivan Skavinsky Skavar.[6]

15. There's a tomb rises up where the Blue Danube rolls,
    And 'graved there in characters clear,
  Are, "Stranger, when passing, oh pray for the soul
    Of Abdul Abulbul Amir."

16. A splash in the Black Sea one dark moonless night,
    Caused ripples to spread wide and far,
  It was made by a sack fitting close to the back,
    Of Ivan Skavinsky Skavar.

17. A Muscovite maiden her lone vigil keeps,
    'Neath the light of the pale polar star,
  And the name that she murmurs so oft, as she weeps,
    Is Ivan Skavinsky Skavar.

Hereafter, follows the additional version of the melody promised at the beginning of this melancholy tale:

[6]Also a deplorable absentee from the naval edition.

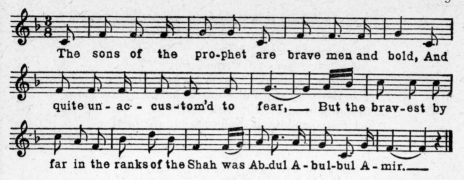

The sons of the pro-phet are brave men and bold, And quite un-ac-cus-tom'd to fear,— But the brav-est by far in the ranks of the Shah was Ab-dul A-bul-bul A-mir.—

KAFOOZALEM

To the same school of pseudo-Orientalism belongs *Kafoozalem*, which, while much shorter than *Abdul*, is even more gruesome in its details, and certainly more pathetic. Brian Hooker, who treasures this song among the rarities in his possession, has initialled the manuscript G. K. W., by which he means to convey that the Lord only knows who wrote it.

In an-cient days there liv'd a Turk, A hor-rid beast, E'en in the East, Who did the Proph-et's ho-ly work, As bar-ber of Je-ru-sa-lem. He had a daugh-ter fair and smirk, Com-plex-ion fair, And light brown hair, With naught a-bout her like a Turk, Ex-cept her name, Ka-fooz-a-lem!

Refrain *(faster)*

My own Ka-fooz-a-lem, Ka-fooz-a-lem, My own Ka-fooz-a-lem, The daugh-ter of the Bar-ber!—

A youth resided near to she—
 His name was Sam—A perfect lamb
Who was of ancient pedigree,
 And came from old Methusalem;
He drove a trade (and prospered well)
 In skins of cats, And worn-out hats;
And ringing at the airy bell,
 He saw, and loved, Kafoozalem.   [*Refrain*]

If Sam had been a Mussulman,
 He might have sold That barber old,
And with a verse of Al Koran
 Have managed to bamboozle 'em;
But no, ah no! Sam tried to scheme—
 Stole up one day—The airy way—
And crept into the Turk's hareem
 To carry off Kafoozalem.   [*Refrain*]

The Old Man had begun to smoke,
 When slaves rushed in With horrid din—
"Marshallah! The dogs your house have broke!
 Oh, do come down, and toozle 'em!"
The Old Man wreathed his face in smiles,
 Said twenty prayers, Then rushed downstairs
To find a man with three old tiles
 A-kissin' of Kafoozalem.   [*Refrain*]

The Barber went to his boudoir,
 And, smiling still With great sang-froid,
He took a bowstring from a drawer,
 And greased it well with goozalum.
The youth and maid he seizéd on,
 And nothing loth, He choked them both,
And threw them in the brook Kedron
 (Which flows hard by Jerusalem).   [*Refrain*]

In ancient days—the story goes—
 When day was done In Babylon,
And when the silver moon arose
 And shone down on Jerusalem,
Amid the crying of the cats—
 A sound that falls From ruin'd walls—
A ghost was seen, with three old hats,
 A-kissin' of Kafoozalem![1]   [*Refrain*]

---

[1] This final stanza should be sung pianissimo.

THE LADY IN CRÊPE

For this song the editor is indebted to Miss Lucie Taussig, herself the editor of *Charm*, but who knows nothing more about it than that it was popular at Amherst forty years ago and is sung to a melody from Donizetti's "Lucia." The influence of the traditional "Spectre Bridegroom" may be seen in the story, but it is difficult to take it seriously, even though there are touches of balladry that might be authentic. Whether real or spurious, it is an amusing song.

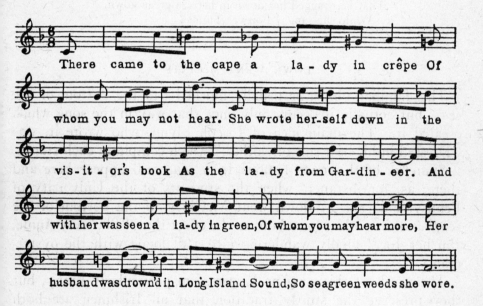

There came to the cape a la-dy in crêpe Of whom you may not hear. She wrote her-self down in the vis-it-or's book As the la-dy from Gar-din-eer. And with her was seen a la-dy in green, Of whom you may hear more, Her husband was drown'd in Long Island Sound, So seagreen weeds she wore.

And as with a clang the dinner bell rang,
　　To the dining hall they sped,
They sat remote at the table de hôte,
　　While the boarders sat at the head.
The boarders proud laughed long and loud,
　　Long laughed each little child,
As they drank their chowder they laughed all the louder,
　　But these neither ate nor smiled.

And as with their lines they sat neath the pines
　　And fished in mute despair,

The fishermen passed and cried through the blast,
 "Oh, give us a lock of your hair!"
"My husband is dead," the lady said,
 "A drownded man is he.
I wish he'd arise with his mild blue eyes
 And speak one word to me."

The words that she muttered were scarcely uttered,
 Her line grew heavy as lead,
When up rose a creature whose every feature
 Resembled her husband dead.
"Come hither to me in the deep blue sea,"
 And he gave such a tug on the line
That he dragged her down in her sea-green gown,
 While she sang, "Forever Thine."

DOWN WENT McGINTY

This familiar phrase is usually finished "to the bottom of the sea," but actually it occurs only once that way in the song which created it. The main idea of Joseph Flynn, who wrote it, was "Dressed in his best suit of clothes," which completes each stanza.

Snatches of this once famous Irish song still appear here and there, as, for instance, when the students of the University of Pennsylvania sing, "Down went McGinty to the bottom of the sea," and then add a line about to the effect that, "She's my Annie, I'm her Joe," finally wandering into a dialogue with the oyster-man.

The words of this song no longer seem particularly funny, but they preserve the sturdy tradition that all Irishmen are both naïve and pugnacious, without which there would be no Irish songs. Have it your own way.

Sunday morning just at nine, Dan McGinty dress'd so fine,
 Stood looking up at a very high stone wall;
When his friend young Pat McCann, says, I'll bet five dollars, Dan,
 I could carry you to the top without a fall;
So on his shoulders he took Dan, to climb the ladder he began,
 And he soon commenc'd to reach up near the top;
When McGinty, cute old rogue, to win the five he did let go,
 Never thinking just how far he'd have to drop.

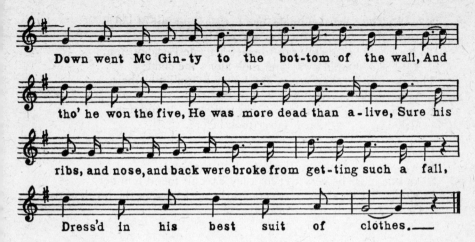

Down went Mc Gin-ty to the bot-tom of the wall, And tho' he won the five, He was more dead than a-live, Sure his ribs, and nose, and back were broke from get-ting such a fall, Dress'd in his best suit of clothes.____

From the hospital Mac went home, when they fixed his broken bone,
    To find he was the father of a child;
So to celebrate it right, his friend he went to invite,
    And he soon was drinking whisky fast and wild;
Then he waddled down the street in his Sunday suit so neat,
    Holding up his head as proud as John the Great;
But in the sidewalk was a hole, to receive a ton of coal,
    That McGinty never saw till just too late.

Chorus:
Down went McGinty to the bottom of the hole,
    Then the driver of the cart gave the load of coal a start,
And it took us half an hour to dig McGinty from the coal,
    Dress'd in his best suit of clothes.

Now McGinty raved and swore, about his clothes he felt so sore,
    And an oath he took he'd kill the man or die;
So he tightly grabb'd his stick and hit the driver a lick,
    Then he raised a little shanty on his eye;
But two policemen saw the muss and they soon join'd in the fuss,
    Then they ran McGinty in for being drunk;
And the Judge says with a smile, we will keep you for a while
    In a cell to sleep upon a prison bunk.

Chorus:
Down went McGinty to the bottom of the jail,
    Where his board would cost him nix and he stay'd exactly six,
They were big long months he stopp'd for no one went his bail,
    Dress'd in his best suit of clothes.

Now McGinty thin and pale, one fine day got out of jail,
  And with joy to see his boy was nearly wild;
To his house he quickly ran to meet his wife Bedaley Ann,
  But she'd skipp'd away and took along the child;
Then he gave up in despair, and he madly pull'd his hair,
  As he stood one day upon the river shore,
Knowing well he couldn't swim, he did foolishly jump in,
  Although water he had never took before.

Chorus:
Down went McGinty to the bottom of the say,[1]
  And he must be very wet for they haven't found him yet,
But they say his ghost comes round the docks before the break of day,
  Dress'd in his best suit of clothes.

THE MAN THAT BROKE THE BANK AT MONTE CARLO

First a European success, and then equally popular in America, *The Man That Broke the Bank at Monte Carlo* has made its contribution to the unforgettable phrases of song literature. The references to the world-famous gambling resort and such Parisian landmarks as the Bois de Boulogne and the Arc de Triomphe are quite obvious. The author and composer was Fred Gilbert, and he did a good job.

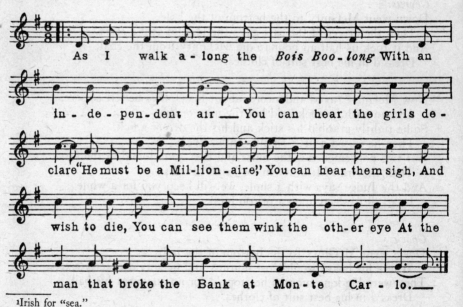

As I walk a-long the *Bois Boo-long* With an in-de-pen-dent air — You can hear the girls de-clare "He must be a Mil-lion-aire;" You can hear them sigh, And wish to die, You can see them wink the oth-er eye At the man that broke the Bank at Mon-te Car-lo.—

[1]Irish for "sea."

I've just got here, thro' Paris, from the sunny southern shore;
I to Monte Carlo went, just to raise my winter's rent;
Dame Fortune smiled upon me as she'd never done before,
And I've now such lots of money, I'm a gent,
Yes, I've now such lots of money I'm a gent.   [*Chorus*]

I stay indoors till after lunch, and then my daily walk
To the great Triumphal Arch is one grand triumphal march.
Observ'd by each observer with the keenness of a hawk,
I'm a mass of money, linen silk and starch,
I'm a mass of money, linen silk and starch.   [*Chorus*]

I patronized the tables at the Monte Carlo hell,
Till they hadn't got a sou for a Christian or a Jew;
So I quickly went to Paris for the charms of mad'moiselle,
Who's the load-stone of my heart, what can I do,
When with twenty tongues she swears that she'll be true?   [*Chorus*]

WHERE DID YOU GET THAT HAT?

Another song which has become a mere catch phrase to us moderns! Written and sung by Joseph J. Sullivan in the late 'Eighties, it had the true Irish flavour. There was an earlier song, *The Hat My Father Wore*, by Daniel McCarthy, which undoubtedly influenced *Where Did You Get That Hat?* with a chorus ending:

From my father's great ancestors it descended, times galore!
It's a relic of old Dacincy,[1] the hat my father wore!

Musically Mr. Sullivan's chorus is founded upon a simple bugle call, quoting almost literally the herald's music in "Lohengrin," and this same tune was recently used again in a song called, *Why Did I Kiss That Girl?* (The Germans have the same tones, with a slightly different arrangement in their popular song, *Du bist verrückt, mein Kind.*)

[1] Decency.

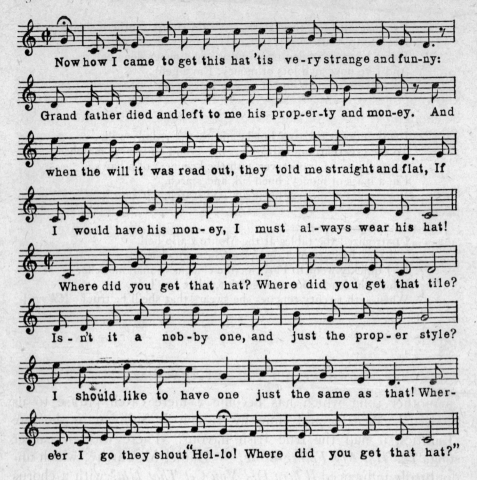

Now how I came to get this hat 'tis ve-ry strange and fun-ny:

Grand father died and left to me his prop-er-ty and mon-ey.   And

when the will it was read out, they told me straight and flat,   If

I   would have his mon-ey, I   must   al-ways wear his hat!

Where did you get that hat? Where did you get that tile?

Is-n't it a nob-by one, and   just the prop-er style?

I   should like to have one   just the same as that! Wher-

e'er I go they shout "Hel-lo! Where did you get that hat?"

If I go to the op'ra-house in the op'ra season,
There's someone sure to shout at me, without the slightest reason.
If I go to a "chowder club," to have a jolly spree;
There's someone in the party, who is sure to shout at me: [Chorus]

At twenty-one I thought I would to my sweetheart be married,
The people in the neighborhood had said too long we'd tarried.
So off to church we went right quick, determined to get wed;
I had not long been in there, when the parson to me said: [Chorus]

THROW HIM DOWN, McCLOSKEY

Another phrase that has already become a mere tradition! Some knowing ones will say, "Maggie Cline's Great Song," and that may be enough (as it was on the original title page). But who was Mc-Closkey and whom did he fight? Let the song reveal its own secrets.

Fight ballads have always been an essential part of folk-literature. In a volume of "Songs of the Shanty Bay," Franz Rickaby prints two logging-camp versions of the historic Heenan-Sayres battle that show much of the spirit and technique of *Throw Him down, McCloskey*. After all, singing and fighting are two essential ingredients of the primitive life, and who wants to be civilized?

The gong! Come on, you, McCloskey!

'Twas down at Dan Mc̈ De-vitt's at the cor-ner of this street, There was to be a prize fight and both par-ties were to meet; To make all the ar-range-ments and see ev-'ry-thing was right, Mc Clos-key and a na-gur were to have a fin-ish fight; The rules were Lon-don Prize Ring and Mc Clos key said he'd try, To bate the na-gur wid one punch or in the ring he'd die; The odds were on Mc Clos-key tho' the bet-ting it was small, 'Twas on Mc Clos-key ten to one, On the na-gur, none at all —

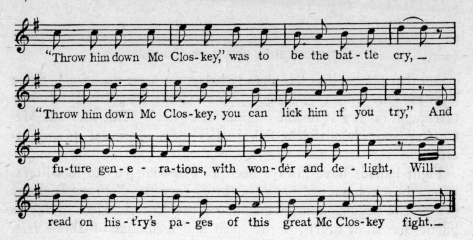

"Throw him down Mc Clos-key," was to be the bat-tle cry, —
"Throw him down Mc Clos-key, you can lick him if you try," And
fu-ture gen-e-ra-tions, with won-der and de-light, Will —
read on his-t'ry's pa-ges of this great Mc Clos-key fight.—

The fighters were to start in at a quarter after eight,
But the nagur did not show up and the hour was getting late;
He sent around a messenger who then went on to say,
That the Irish crowd would jump him and he couldn't get fair play;
Then up steps Pete McCracken, and said that he would fight,
Stand up or rough and tumble if McCloskey didn't bite!
McCloskey says, "I'll go you," then the seconds got in place,
And the fighters started in to decorate each other's face. [*Chorus*]

They fought like two hyenas till the forty-seventh round,
They scattered blood enough around by gosh, to paint the town,
McCloskey got a mouthful of poor McCracken's jowl.
McCracken hollered, "Murthur" and his seconds hollered, "Foul!"
The friends of both the fighters that instant did begin
To fight and at each other the whole party started in,
You couldn't tell the diff'rence in your fighters if you'd try,
McCracken lost his upper lip, McCloskey lost an eye. [*Chorus*]

PATTERNS OF PARODY

All through America's popular song literature will be found
certain simple models of melody which have served over and over
again for every conceivable type of text. There is, for example,
the pattern of all "echo songs" (see p. 61) whose most familiar words
begin, "And when I die (And when I die), Don't bury me at all
(Don't bury me at all)" (with a barber-shop chord). This primitive tune also had a lyric called *The Goat*, which contained one of

the Olympian jokes of the past, still emerging occasionally in story form.

> One day that goat felt frisk and fine,
> Ate three red shirts from off the line.
> The man he grabbed him by the back,
> And tied him to a railroad track.
>
> But when the train hove into sight,
> That goat grew pale and green with fright.
> He heaved a sigh, as if in pain,
> *Coughed up those shirts and flagged the train.*

Hinky Dee was the name of a forgotten ancestor of all the songs of the *Ain't gonna Rain no More, Show me the Way to go home* type. Variants of this and the preceding melody have probably supported more parodies and topical verses than all the other songs of the world put together. *Three Leaves of Shamrock* was another old-timer that produced more than its share of parodies.

When our forefathers were in a mood for something a bit shocking, they were quite likely to spring this one, to the tune of *The Last Rose of Summer:*

> Little Johnnie had a mirror, And he ate the back all off,
> Thinking rashly, in his terror, It would cure the whooping-cough.
> Some days later Johnnie's mother Weeping said to Mrs. Brown:
> "'Twas a chilly day for Johnnie When the mercury went down."[1]

---

[1]The significance of this joke is that mercury is used to paint the backs of mirrors and also in thermometers. Ha-ha!

THE GOLDEN AGE

WITH the opening of the nebulous 'Nineties came the Golden Age of popular song-writing in America, and it lasted well on into the Twentieth Century before jazz and the radio got in their deadly work and substituted quantity for quality. The successful publishers of popular music all acquired their real headway during the 'Nineties and for the first time it was discovered that a song of wide appeal could make a great deal of money for all concerned.

The practice of "plugging" received its start in the 'Nineties, developing a type of musician that is still active, for the sole purpose of demonstrating and "boosting" certain numbers on every possible occasion. The song-pluggers have worked in the professional rooms of the publishers, in department stores, in theatres, at ball games, at political meetings, in fact, anywhere that people could be made to listen.

The era of song-slides also began in the 'Nineties, and this marked the real introduction of the screen as a propagandist for music, and clearly foretold the reign of the motion picture. Where theatrical managers were once content to have each line of a song illustrated by some garishly coloured scene from the "magic lantern," the modern revue achieves a pretentious effect by using elaborate action, costumes, and scenery for precisely the same purpose. Incidentally, song-slides are still popular in the movies.

Sentimental ballads were all the rage up to the close of the Nineteenth Century, after which it became the fashion to spoof them and turn to a sophisticated brand of comedy instead, in spite of which the naïve "Story-song" of human interest still achieves a wider distribution than any other type.

THOSE DEAR WALTZ GIRLS

The early 'Nineties saw a whole series of songs written around the names or nicknames of their heroines, all in a popular waltz form. Harry Dacre was the star contributor to the movement, with *Elsie from Chelsea* and *Daisy Bell*, the latter, perhaps, better known to-day by its final line, *A Bicycle Built for Two*.

Maude Nugent crashed into the limelight with *Sweet Rosie O'Grady*, which is still a steady seller, while from England came Michael Nolan's *Little Annie Rooney*, revived by the Witmarks not long ago in connection with a Mary Pickford film. From England also we secured *Comrades*, which was musically in the same class, although it did not use the girl-technique, and *Doris*, a really fine waltz by George Maywood. Anita Owens's *Sweet Bunch of Daisies* belongs to the same general school of song-writing, and *Sweet Marie*, by escaping from the hackneyed waltz rhythm, still stands out as a most successful "girl song."

Elsie from Chelsea is worth quoting, not only because of its catchy refrain, but because Dacre succeeded in avoiding the mushiness of most of the contemporary lyrics without being cynical or falling into burlesque.   This is the chorus:

Riding one morning, my fare I'd just paid,
  Oh, what a lovely day!
Gave up my seat to a sweet little maid,
  Oh, what a lovely day!
Tho' she was really a stranger to me,
Soon in a deep conversation were we;
Told me her name was E-L-S-I-E
  From C-H-E-L-S-E-A. [*Chorus*]

Said she had nowhere partic'lar to go,—
  Oh, what a lovely day!
Taking the hint, I was not very slow,
  Oh, what a gorgeous day!
Soon we were gushing as lovers can gush,
Told her I loved her, but she answered, "Hush!"
Then when I kissed her, she said, with a blush,
  "Oh, what a beautiful day!" [*Chorus*]

Went and we supped in a well-known café,
    Oh, what a lovely night!
I was bankrupt before we came away,
    Oh, what a lovely night!
P'r'aps you will guess that it ended in strife,
Got a black eye, and escaped with my life,—
Nonsense! The end is that she is my wife,
    We have been married to-day. [*Chorus*]

His *Daisy Bell*, like most of the others in this group, still adorns the song sheets of Kiwanis and Rotary, and brings a response from almost any singing crowd.[1] The familiar chorus is the perfect expression of the tandem age and makes it possible to forgive such lines in the verses as:

"I will stand by you in 'wheel' or woe,
    You'll be the 'belle' which I'll ring, you know."

Lyn Udall produced one of the last of the waltz-girl songs in 1898, *Just One Girl*. Obviously her name was Pearl. In the same year he added *Just as the Sun Went Down* to the literature of the Spanish War. Both were published by the Witmarks, and both did exceedingly well.

TA-RA-RA BOOM-DER-É

The habit of using meaningless syllables in a chorus, originating in the "burden" of typical folk-song, and reaching its height in the English madrigals, has cropped up a number of times in American popular music, but never more violently than in *Ta-ra-ra Boom-der-é*. (The title is generally quoted *Ta-ra-ra-ra Boom-de-ay*, but this loses the stylish effect of the French accent, besides putting in an extra beat.)

It was written by Henry J. Sayers, a theatrical press agent, for the "minstrel farce comedy, 'Tuxedo,'" and the dedication was to Miss Hattie F. Townley, of Washington, D. C. If she represents the heroine of the song, Miss Townley was distinctly ahead of her

---

[1]Charlie Lawlor's *Sidewalks of New York*, which became a campaign song for Al Smith in 1924, is so similar musically, that people often switch from one song to the other, without knowing which one they are singing.

time.   She might even have told the blonde Miss Lorelei Lee a few things.

It is said that Sayers first heard this chorus in a St. Louis cabaret, run by a negress, "Babe" Connors.   Outside of the gibberish, the words were unspeakable. He substituted polite verses, and eventually the song reached Lottie Collins, who made it a riot in England by singing the first part ultra-demurely and then going into a kicking chorus with what was undoubtedly the jazziest effect of 1891.

This strange, nonsensical chorus had the doubtful advantage of never really coming to an end, so that if a crowd once started singing it, the noise could go on indefinitely, and usually did.

The song travelled all over the world, and was printed again and again in a variety of foreign languages. Christopher Morley included it in his Hoboken revival of *The Black Crook* (although this was a chronological anachronism), following the success of *After Dark*, whose saloon scene brought in, among other old-timers, *We Never Speak as We Pass By* (p. 61) and *Oh, Fred, Tell Them to Stop* (p. 69).

Sayers renewed his copyright in 1918, and vigorously defended it until the day of his death, coincident with a court decree recognizing *Ta-ra-ra Boom-der-é* as his property.   The song is now sponsored by the indefatigable Jerry Vogel, who specializes in the revival of old numbers, with the co-operation of Frank Crumit and George Cohan. It is beginning to be heard again on the radio, and may in time enjoy such a Phoenix-lifting as was recently demonstrated by *The Man on the Flying Trapeze* and *There is a Tavern in the Town*.

Meanwhile Theodore Metz, composer of *A Hot Time in the Old Town Tonight*, insists that he should get some credit for the so-called melody of *Ta-ra-ra Boom-der-é*, as he was the one who actually wrote it down, after a wild night at the Connors place.   According to Metz's story, he woke up in the same bed with Sayers, whose first question on regaining consciousness was "Have you got that tune we heard last night?"   But what with the vo-deo-do and boop-a-doop school, nonsense syllables and nonsensical tunes are an old story by this time.

Parodies of *Ta-ra-ra Boom-der-é* sprang up almost immediately. Most of them were harmless, as, for example, the one about the goat (still a favourite animal with song-writers):

There was a goat, a one-eyed goat,
He was old enough to vote,
Tomato cans were his delight,
Chewed bill-posters day and night,
Butted through a high stone wall,
Terrified the neighbors all
But Maria, fat and fair,
Standing by the wash-tub there.
And she hollered "Boom de-ay,
Ta-ra-ra-ra boom de-ay."

There was another verse about a little boy who climbed a tree for peaches, and one about a girl from Baltimore, "street car runs right by the door," and ending with the brilliant suggestion, "Johnny get your hair cut Pompadour."

For those who would like a taste of the more serious girl love songs of the 'nineties, a revival of *Just One Girl* is hereby suggested.

JUST ONE GIRL

I'm in love with a sweet lit-tle girl-ie__ on-ly one,__ __ on-ly one; __ I meet her each morn-ing quite ear-ly,__ __ rain or sun,__ rain or sun; __ To work we go walk-ing to-geth-er,__ Just as gay, __ as can be,__ We're tru-ly two birds of a feath-er__ Just one lit-tle girl and me.__

Chorus

Just one girl,__ on-ly just one girl,__ There are oth-ers, I

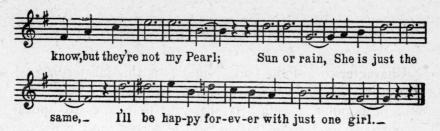

know, but they're not my Pearl;   Sun or rain, She is just the

same, _   I'll be hap-py for-ev-er with just one girl._

To be married we're old enough plenty,
    She and I, she and I;
She's eighteen and I will be twenty,
    Bye and bye, bye and bye;
Although we are short as to money,
    What care we, what care we?
There are only two flies in the honey
    Just one little girl and me. [Chorus]

THE CAT CAME BACK

Tony Pastor, Julia Mackey, and others combined to make this song title a household phrase. It gathered additional verses as it grew in favour, and it had the virtue of being adaptable to almost any occasion and endless parody.

The various stanzas told in turn how Mr. Johnson's cat survived successively a boot-jack, a brick-bat, electrocution on a telegraph wire, the collapse of a balloon, a cyclone, a train wreck, and a charge of dynamite. The final verse announced, with a touch of professional jealousy, that the cat eventually dropped dead when an organ-grinder played *Ta-ra-ra Boom-der-é*.

Here is the chorus:

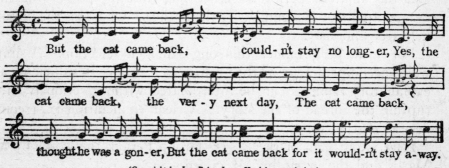

But the cat came back,   could-n't stay no long-er, Yes, the

cat came back,   the ver-y next day, The cat came back,

thought he was a gon-er, But the cat came back for it would-n't stay a-way.

THE LITTLE LOST CHILD

Characteristic of the Gay 'Nineties is this masterpiece of sentimentality, which, in its day, rivalled *After the Ball* and other waltz hits in popular esteem. It was the first song to appear with coloured slides for illustration on the screen, and thus started a custom which served the professional pluggers long and faithfully. The man who manufactured the first slides was George H. Thomas, a Brooklyn photographer. William Fox, who still keeps up his interest in pictures, ran a slide exchange on Fourteenth Street at the time.

The Little Lost Child was important also as creator of the partnership of Edward B. Marks and Joseph W. Stern, who met as drummers on the road. (Marks was selling "notions," and he still has some good ones.) The song was founded upon an actual occurrence (truth is stranger than fiction, but not so convincing), and it persuaded its collaborators to go regularly into the music business, the firm, like its parent song, dating from the year 1894. It continues to-day as the Edward B. Marks Music Company, and has been responsible for a vast number of successes in the newer as well as the older style.

The best modern interpreter of *The Little Lost Child*, so far as the editor knows, is Franklin P. Adams, of the *World's* "Conning Tower." He sings it in an utterly expressionless voice and with immobile features, which is quite an achievement for anybody. It is in this way that such songs can be presented most effectively, and the amateur performer is warned not to "point" the lines exaggeratedly or overemphasize the pathos. Of course the pictures help tremendously.

For casual performance, this song is an ideal selection. A simple waltz accompaniment of the "tum-te-te" variety is sufficient, and explanatory remarks can be interpolated without seriously interrupting the thread of the story. A clear enunciation is of course desirable at all times.

Here is our gem of the Rogers Group Period, the words by Mr. Marks and the music by Mr. Stern:

A pass-ing po-lice-man found a lit-tle
"'Twas all through a quar-rel mad-ly jea-lous

child,___ She walked be-side him, dried her
she,___ Vowed then to leave me, wom-an-

tears and smiled.___ Said he to her kind-ly,
like you see.[5]___ Oh, how I loved—her,

"Now you must not cry,___ I will find your ma-
grief near drove me wild".___ "Pa-pa you are cry-

ma, for you bye-and-bye."___ At the sta-tion
ing," lisped the lit-tle child.[6]___ Sud-den-ly the

when he[1] asked her for her name,___ And she
door of the sta-tion o-pened wide,___ "Have you

an-swered "Jen-nie," it made him ex-
seen my dar-ling?" an an-xious moth-er

[1]F. P. A. always uses a strongly syncopated "whennie," and repeats the effect with "Jennie," so that his hearers will not overlook the rhyme.

[5]The child is undoubtedly aware of this habit of womanhood.

[6]Probably the child merely said, "Cwying," for what is so rare as a lisp without an s?

claim:___   "At last of your moth-er
cried.___   Hus-band and wife then

I have now a trace;___ Your___ lit-tle
meet-ing face to face;___ All is soon for-

fea-tures bring back her sweet face."___
giv-en, in one fond em-brace.___

CHORUS

"Do not fear my lit-tle dar-ling, And I[2] will

take you right home.___ Come and sit down close be-

side me, No more from me[3] you shall roam.___ For

you were a babe in arms, when your moth-er left

me one day.___ Left me at home, de-sert-ed, a-

lone,[4] And took you my child a-way."___

(*Copyright, 1894, by Jos. W. Stern & Co. Used by permission.*)

[2]Second time "we."   [3]Second time "us."

[4]This is the place to break into harmony, if available.

MY MOTHER WAS A LADY *or* IF JACK WERE ONLY HERE

Probably Ed Marks was at least pointing his tongue in the general direction of his cheek when he wrote the words of this song in 1896. *The Little Lost Child* had produced its share of hilarity as well as tears, and its publishers wisely decided to capitalize the jocosities of contemporary columnists and cartoonists.

Joe Stern, whose partnership with Marks had already prospered, wrote the music, using the current trick of a verse in four-four time, followed by a conventional waltz chorus. *My Mother Was a Lady* is also obviously a "slide song," with each stilted line perfectly fitted to screen illustration.

It originated in a little German restaurant on Twenty-first Street, New York, where the singers, actors, and music publishers of the day often met for luncheon. A new waitress appeared there one day, a buxom, rosy-cheeked Lancashire girl, who immediately became the object of the regular customers' wit. Suddenly she burst into tears, crying out that nobody would dare insult her if her brother Jack were only there, and adding defiantly, "My mother was a lady." Meyer Cohen, one of the popular song-pluggers, immediately saw the possibilities of the line and prevailed upon Marks to write the lyric on the spot.

Cohen introduced the song successfully the very next day, at Tony Pastor's theatre, and later it became one of the biggest hits in the repertoire of Lottie Gilson, the "Little Magnet" of vaudeville. It was revived not long ago as entr'acte music for "East Lynne," at the Provincetown Theatre, along with *Take Back Your Gold*, sung by Louise Bradley. Hundreds of requests were received at the time for the original words and music, so here they are:

Two drummers sat at din-ner, in a grand ho-tel one day, While

din-ing they were chat-ting in a jol-ly sort of way, And

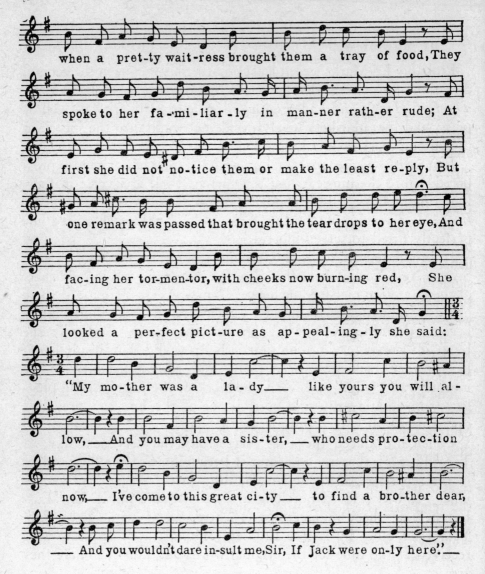

when a pret-ty wait-ress brought them a tray of food, They

spoke to her fa-mi-liar-ly in man-ner rath-er rude; At

first she did not no-tice them or make the least re-ply, But

one remark was passed that brought the tear drops to her eye, And

fac-ing her tor-men-tor, with cheeks now burn-ing red, She

looked a per-fect pict-ure as ap-peal-ing-ly she said:

"My mo-ther was a la-dy__ like yours you will al-

low,__ And you may have a sis-ter,__ who needs pro-tec-tion

now,__ I've come to this great ci-ty__ to find a bro-ther dear,

__ And you wouldn't dare in-sult me, Sir, If Jack were on-ly here."__

It's true one touch of nature, it makes the whole world kin,[1]
And ev'ry word she uttered seemed to touch their hearts within,
They sat there stunned and silent, until one cried in shame,
"Forgive me, Miss! I meant no harm, pray tell me what's your name?"
She told him and he cried again, "I know your brother too,
Why we've been friends for many years and he often speaks of you,[2]

[1]How true that is!
[2]People believed this one in 1896.

He'll be so glad to see you, and if you'll only wed,[3]
I'll take you to him as my wife, for I love you since you said: [*Chorus*]

THE FATAL WEDDING

Gussie L. Davis, who wrote *The Fatal Wedding* and several other big successes of the early 'Nineties, was a Negro, and a male in spite of his name.   His first song was called *Poverty Row*, and was published by Ed Marks and Joe Stern.   He also had one called *The Lighthouse by the Sea*.   But his real hits were *In the Baggage Coach Ahead* and the connubial classic below.

The Fatal Wedding, dedicated "to the Utica *Tribune*" (perhaps in honour of its Marriages, Births, Deaths column), was first published by Spaulding, Kornder & Co., with the copyright later assigned to M. D. Swisher of Philadelphia.   Ed Marks had been kind to the composer in his lean years, and after the death of Davis, his widow saw to it that the heart-throb specialist acquired the rights to the great *Baggage Coach* song, which is still popular, while *The Fatal Wedding* also appears to-day in the Marks list of Old Time Favourites.

The words are by W. H. Windom.   There is a maestoso introduction, consisting of the opening strains of Mendelssohn's Wedding March, followed by an imitation of chimes, left pretty much to the discretion of the pianist.

The waltz music of the verse should be taken at a fairly lively tempo, but with a suppressed and portentous tone of voice.   When the refrain is reached, a broad, passionate style is in order.   Between stanzas, the last line may be repeated by the piano, in octaves, with little doo-dab decorations to the closing measures.   It is all very poignant.

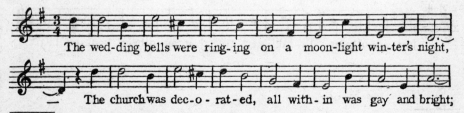

The wed-ding bells were ring-ing on a moon-light win-ter's night,

The church was dec-o-rat-ed, all with-in was gay and bright;

[3]This, of course, was the least he could do under the circumstances—the *amende honorable* to the retort courteous!   Ah, those were the days of romance.

A moth-er with her ba-by came and saw the lights a-glow, __ She thought of how those same bells chimed for her three years a-go! __ "I'd like to be ad-mit-ted sir," she told the sex-ton old, __ Just for the sake of ba-by, to pro-tect him from the cold, __ He told her that the wed-ding there was for the rich and grand, __ And with the ea-ger watch-ing crowd, out-side she'd have to stand. __

While the wed-ding bells were ring-ing, while the bride and groom were there, March-ing up the aisle to-geth-er, __ As the or-gan pealed an air; Tell-ing tales of fond af-fec-tion,[1] __ Vow-ing nev-er more to part, Just an-oth-er fa-tal wed-ding, Just an-oth-er brok-en heart.

---

[1]This habit of brides and bridegrooms, while marching up the aisle, has long been noticeable. In fact, it was getting to be a public nuisance about the time this song was written.

She begged the sexton once again to let her pass inside.
"For baby's sake you may step in," the gray-haired man replied;
"If any one knows reason why this couple should not wed,
Speak now, or hold your peace forever," soon the preacher said!
"I must object,"[2] the woman cried, with voice so meek and mild,
"The bridegroom is my husband, sir, and this our little child."
"What proof have you?" the preacher asked. "My infant," she replied.[3]
She raised her babe, then knelt to pray, the little one had died.[4]   [*Chorus*]

The parents of the bride then took the outcast by the arm.
"We'll care for you through life," they said, "you've saved our child from harm."
The outcast wife, the bride and parents, quickly drove away,
The husband died by his own hand, before the break of day![5]
No wedding feast was spread that night, two graves were made next day,
One for the little baby, and in one the father lay.
The story has been often told, by firesides warm and bright,
Of bride and groom, of outcast, and the fatal wedding night.   [*Chorus*]

IN THE BAGGAGE COACH AHEAD

It is rather difficult to laugh at this other masterpiece of Gussie Davis. In the light of such modern contributions to the musical slush fund as *Ten Little Fingers and Ten Little Toes*, etc., it has a sincerity of sentiment that defies sophisticated mockery.

The story of the young father travelling eastward with a troublesome child, while the dead mother lay in the baggage coach ahead, was founded upon fact. Not long ago, the newspapers carried a report of the death in Kansas City of Mrs. Nettie Klapmeyer, who was the baby of the actual journey. It may be surmised that Davis himself was the Pullman porter on the train, and had plenty of opportunity to take in the whole situation.

He wrote both the words and the music of this song, and its vogue is by no means over, as modern dance orchestras have testi-

---

[2]Evidently well schooled in the legal formulæ of the day.

[3]Or, as the old adage has it, "The proof of the wedding is the offspring."

[4]This turns the song suddenly from good, clean fun into stark tragedy. Thereafter the events follow thick and fast. We can hardly wait.

[5]A graceful gesture, under the circumstances.

fied.   The lines are mostly straightforward and honestly pathetic, and the waltz melody is rather above the average.

The Baggage Coach Ahead has recently been reissued by the Edward B. Marks Music Company in response to a general demand, by no means limited to the scoffers.

Here is the chorus:

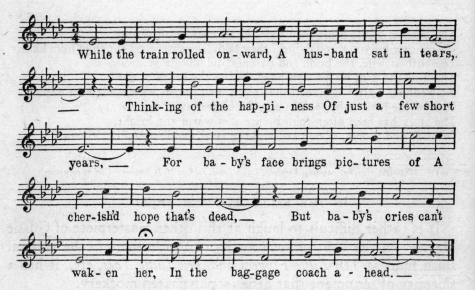

While the train rolled on-ward, A hus-band sat in tears,. — Think-ing of the hap-pi-ness Of just a few short years, — For ba-by's face brings pic-tures of A cher-ish'd hope that's dead, — But ba-by's cries can't wak-en her, In the bag-gage coach a-head. —

(*Copyright, 1896, by Howley, Haviland & Co., assigned, 1924, to Edw. B. Marks Music Co.   Used by permission.*)

THE MOTH AND THE FLAME

While this bit of nature study has always been a popular subject with sentimentalists, it was brought specifically to the attention of the American public by a play, in which Effie Shannon and Herbert Kelcey were the stars.   George Taggart and Max S. Witt collaborated in taking advantage of this dramatic success, and their ballad made many a kitchen sink quiver with sympathy before it died of auto-intoxication.

The plot is similar to that of *The Fatal Wedding*, but more subtly told.

At a gay re-cep-tion giv-en in a man-sion grand and old, A young man met the girl he used to know;— And once a-gain the sto-ry of his hon-est love he told, The love he'd cher-ished since long years a - go.— But she sighed and sad-ly mur-mur'd that her child-hood love was past, That soon an-oth-er man she was to wed.— The lov-er knew the oth-er man al-read-y had a wife. He bade fare-well, but as he went, he said:[1] "The Moth and the Flame play'd a game[2] one day, The game of a wo-man's heart;— And the Moth that play'd was a maid, they say, The Flame was a bad man's art.— The Moth nev-er knew, as she

[1]We can hardly forgive the hero for being so cryptic about it. Probably the girl had never studied insectology, and possessed no copy of the "Dictionary of Phrase and Fable."

[2]This chorus is one of the early examples of inner rhyming, which has become almost a commonplace in modern technique. Musically, it has more originality than have most of its contemporaries in the waltz field.

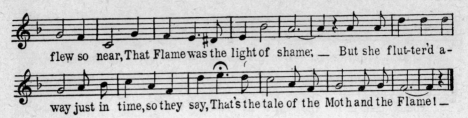

flew so near, That Flame was the light of shame; — But she flut-ter'd a-

way just in time, so they say, That's the tale of the Moth and the Flame! —

The maiden did not understand the fable that he told,
    A church was soon arrayed in holy state,
A couple at the altar stood before the crowd of guests,
    When a woman scream'd, "Stop! ere it is too late."
The villain turn'd and saw his wife and rudely struck her down,[3]
    Denouncing her as an imposter bold;
But the girl threw off the bridal wreath. "You coward," then she cried,
    "My true love warned me when this tale he told:" [Chorus]

(Copyright by Edw. B. Marks Music Co. Used by permission.)

THE BOSTON BURGLAR

The fascinating subject of crime has provided endless material for the singers and song-writers of the world. There is a very old song about Captain Kidd, which produces innumerable verses to point the moral of that interesting pirate's villainies. The famous Captain is quoted in part, as follows:

Don't, for the sake of gold, lose your souls.

. . . .

I cursed my father dear, and her that did me bear,
    And so wickedly did swear, when I sailed.

. . . .

My repentance lasted not, my vows I soon forgot,
    Damnation's my just lot, as I sailed.

. . . .

Come all ye young and old, you're welcome to my gold,
    For by it I've lost my soul, and must die.

. . . .

---

[3]Not only that, but he did not even have the grace to commit suicide, as exemplified by the near-husband of *The Fatal Wedding*. Altogether a bad business. It is to be hoped the honest lover found the girl eventually, and that the first wife recovered sufficiently to sock the villain as he deserved.

Take warning now by me, and shun bad company,
Lest you come to hell with me, for I must die.[1]

All this, of course, is very helpful to any one of uncertain ethics. There is a modern equivalent in a recent ballad concerning the death of Gerald Chapman.

The Boston Burglar is typical of its school, and it has more than a suggestion of the true ballad spirit. M. J. Fitzpatrick is credited with its authorship, and while the burglar's individual crimes are not described in detail, it presents a thoroughly enticing picture. With the best intentions in the world, this song could hardly be expected to keep many people out of jail.

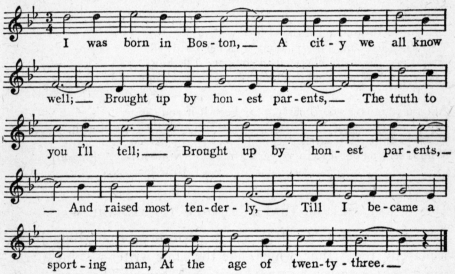

I was born in Bos-ton,— A cit-y we all know well;— Brought up by hon-est par-ents,— The truth to you I'll tell;— Brought up by hon-est par-ents,— And raised most ten-der-ly,— Till I be-came a sport-ing man, At the age of twen-ty-three.—

[1]Quite in the spirit of *Captain Kidd*, and with a suggestion of its actual tune, is the later *Sammy Hall* (or, more respectably, *Samuel Hall*) usually sung by those who have an overwhelming desire to curse, without the courage to let it out. Here are a few of the stanzas:

My name is Sammy Hall, Sammy Hall;
My name is Sammy Hall, and I hate you one and all;
You're a gang of muckers all—
Damn your eyes.

Up the gallows I must go, I must go;
Up the gallows I must go, with my friends all down below
Saying—"Sam, we told you so!"—
Damn their eyes.

I saw Nellie in the crowd, in the crowd,
I saw Nellie in the crowd, an' I hollered—right out loud—
"Say, Nellie, ain't yuh proud—
Damn your eyes."

My character was taken, and I was sent to jail,
My friends found that it was in vain to get me out on bail;
The jury found me guilty, the clerk he wrote it down,
The judge then passed my sentence and I was sent to Charlestown.

See my agèd father, a-standing at the bar;
Likewise my agèd mother, a-tearing of her hair;
Yes, tearing of her old grey locks while the tears came pouring down,
Saying, "Son, dear son, what have you done, that you're sent to Charlestown?"

I was put on board an Eastern train, one cold December day,
At ev'ry station that we passed I'd hear the people say:
"There goes the Boston burglar, in strong chains he is bound,
For some crime or another, he is off to Charlestown."

Is a girl in Boston, a girl that I love well,
And when I get my liberty, along with her I'll dwell,
And if ever I get my liberty, bad company I'll shun,
Likewise night prowling, gambling, and also drinking rum.[1]

All you who have your liberty, pray keep it if you can,
And don't go 'round the streets at night to break the laws of man;
For if you do you'll surely rue, and find yourself like me,
Who is serving out a twenty-year term, in the penitentiary. [*Chorus*]

THE PICTURE THAT IS TURNED TOWARD THE WALL

In 1891, Charles Graham saw a performance of "Blue Jeans,"
a play by Joe Arthur, which, like the same writer's "Still Alarm,"
ran a whole season at the Fourteenth Street Theatre. In this
rural drama there was a scene in which the farmer, whose daughter
has run away from home, turned her picture to the wall.

This situation suggested the song, *The Picture That Is Turned
toward the Wall*, and Graham wrote it, both words and music, for
Julius Witmark, who was then singing with Russell's Comedians
in "The City Directory."   Witmark took it all the way out to the
coast, and it became the first big ballad hit of his firm, the start of
a tradition which has continued to the present day.

Later it was taken up by many other singers, including Andrew

---

[1]Captain Kidd has it all over the Boston Burglar in his ability to enumerate and specify crimes.

Mack, who, at the time of this writing, was still playing in "Abie's Irish Rose." (No, not continuously since 1891.)

The same idea, on a broader scale, was used in Charpentier's "Louise" many years later, and proved just as effective in grand opera as in the more naïve ballad style. The song held its own against all the great narrative lyrics of the 'Nineties, and will be remembered affectionately by most of the fathers and mothers of the present generation. The music of the verses doesn't matter particularly.

> Far away beyond the glamour of the city and its strife,
> There's a quiet little homestead by the sea,
> Where a tender, loving lassie used to live a happy life,
> Contented in her home as she could be.
> Not a shadow ever seemed to cloud the sunshine of her youth,
> And they thought no sorrow could her life befall;
> But she left them all one evening, and their sad hearts knew the truth,
> When her father turned her picture to the wall.

> There's a name that's nev-er spok-en, and a moth-er's heart half brok-en, There is just an-oth-er miss-ing from the old home, that is all; There is still a mem-'ry liv-ing, there's a fath-er un-for-giv-ing, and a pic-ture that is turn'd to-ward the wall.

> They have laid away each token of the one who ne'er returns,
> Every trinket, every ribbon that she wore,
> Though it seems so long ago now, yet the lamp of hope still burns,
> And her mother prays to see her child once more.
> Though no tidings ever reached them what her life or lot may be,
> Though they sometimes think she's gone beyond recall;
> There's a tender recollection of a face they never see,
> In the picture that is turned toward the wall. [*Chorus*]

Another spectacular hit by Charles Graham was *If the Waters Could Speak as They Flow*, a song which runs the gamut of human experience in a thoroughly picturesque fashion. Meanwhile, Ford and Bratton had written *I love you in the same old Way*, *Darling Sue*, also for the Witmarks, and *The Sunshine of Paradise Alley*, whose chorus, whether intentionally or not, opens with a phrase directly borrowed from Mascagni's "Cavalleria Rusticana."

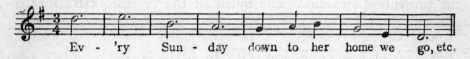

Ev - 'ry   Sun - day   down   to   her   home   we   go, etc.

Closely related to the song literature of convicts, pictures turned toward the wall, and all the recognized deplorability of vice is a ballad, now rarely heard, called *Picture Eighty-four* (also known as *Convict Eighty-four*). It is in the mental collections of Howard Dietz, of Metro-Goldwyn, and Shelley Hamilton, the composer of *Lord Jeffrey Amherst*. This version has their authority:

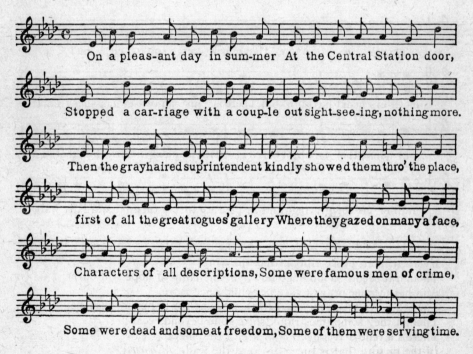

On a pleas-ant day in sum-mer At the Central Station door,

Stopped a car-riage with a coup-le out sight-see-ing, nothing more.

Then the grayhaired suprintendent kindly showed them thro' the place,

first of all the great rogues' gallery Where they gazed on many a face,

Characters of all descriptions, Some were famous men of crime,

Some were dead and some at freedom, Some of them were serving time.

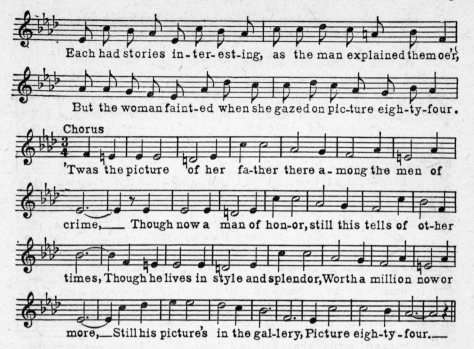

Each had stories in-ter-est-ing, as the man explained them oe'r,

But the woman faint-ed when she gazed on pic-ture eigh-ty-four.

Chorus

'Twas the picture of her fa-ther there a-mong the men of

crime,___ Though now a man of hon-or, still this tells of ot-her

times, Though he lives in style and splendor, Worth a million now or

more,___ Still his picture's in the gal-ler-y, Picture eigh-ty-four.___

"Listen, I will tell the story," then the sup'erintendent said,
"Years ago before your mother to your father, child, was wed,
She'd a brother rash and wayward, foolishly he forged a check,
And the single act of folly threaten'd all his life to wreck,
Then your father's noble nature rose to shield her brother's name,
For the sake of her he loved so, took upon himself the blame,
Gave himself then up to justice, ''Twas I who forged the check,' said he,
And spent weary years in prison, that your uncle might be free." [Chorus]

THE BAND PLAYED ON

Outside of the fact that practically everybody has heard the
first two lines of the chorus of this song (although few can sing
them correctly), *The Band Played On* is important as the first real
hit to be put over by a newspaper, in this case the New York
World. John F. Palmer wrote the words, and the music is by
Charles B. Ward.

Matt Casey formed a social club that beat the town for style,
    And hired for a meeting place a hall;
When pay day came around each week they greased the floor with wax,
    And danced with noise and vigor at the ball.

Each Saturday you'd see them dressed up in Sunday clothes,
  Each lad would have his sweetheart by his side.
When Casey led the first grand march they all would fall in line,
  Behind the man who was their joy and pride.   For—

Ca-sey would waltz with a straw-ber-ry blonde, And the
Band played on, ___ He'd glide 'cross the floor with the
girl he a - dor'd, and the Band played on, ___ But his
brain was so load-ed it near-ly ex - plod-ed, The
poor girl would shake with a - larm. ___ He'd ne'er leave the
girl with the straw-ber-ry curls, And the Band played on. ___

Such kissing in the corner and such whisp'ring in the hall,
  And telling tales of love behind the stairs—
As Casey was the favorite and he that ran the ball,
  Of kissing and love making did his share.
At twelve o'clock exactly they all would fall in line,
  Then march down to the dining-hall and eat.
But Casey would not join them although ev'ry thing was fine,
  But he stayed upstairs and exercised his feet.   For—   [Chorus]

Now when the dance was over and the band played "Home Sweet Home,"
  They played a tune at Casey's own request.
He thank'd them very kindly for the favors they had shown,
  Then he'd waltz once with the girl that he loved best.
Most all the friends are married that Casey used to know,
  And Casey too has taken him a wife.
The blonde he used to waltz and glide with on the ballroom floor,
  Is happy Missis Casey now for life.   For—   [Chorus]

Lovers of Irish songs still know how to sing *Tim Toolan* ("The fat man that came from Tipperary"), written and sung in 1893 by "the great J. W. Kelly," with a verse which capitally imitated a brass band in two strains and an interlude. To the same year belongs *McKenna's Insurance*, a nonsense song of the type which should be sung all the way through or not at all. In the repertoire of Bill McKenna, who knows both of these Irish masterpieces, is also *Duffy's Blunders* (based upon the actual malapropisms of a New York judge) and *Upper Ten and Lower Five*, which is not a sleeping-car song, but the dialogue between a nobleman and a beggar, full of sententiousness, and ending:

> "Well, as you seem to be hard up, good man,
>   A gold sovereign I will give."
> "Ah, you rich men, sir, hardly know
>   How half of this world do live."

ARE YOU THE O'REILLY?

No group of Irish songs would be complete without Pat Rooney's classic *Are you the O'Reilly?* The chorus is enough as a reminder:

Are you the O'Reil-ly that keeps this ho-tel? Are you the O' Reil-ly they speak of so well? Are you the O' Reil-ly they speak of so high-ly? Gor blime me O' Reil-ly, You are look-ing well.

(Copyright by Leo Feist, Inc. Used by permission.)

DO, DO, MY HUCKLEBERRY, DO

This curious phrase sounds familiar to many a modern ear, but few of us remember what it was all about. Actually, *Do, Do, My Huckleberry, Do* was one of the first highly sophisticated songs. It preached a hard-boiled philosophy that even a modern business man could not consider half-hearted, and its unyielding cynicism was a scarcely veiled protest against the moralizings and sentimentalities of its time.

The Dillons, Harry and John, wrote the words and music respectively, and probably they didn't intend to be taken literally. At any rate, when Julius Witmark turned it over to Harry Conor, in "A Trip to Chinatown" (which also contained those amazing successes, *After the Ball*, and *The Bowery*), *Do, Do, My Huckleberry Do* was an immediate hit. It is said that the topical verses used to be changed every week. Sing it all the way through and you will learn something.

A fa-ther to his on-ly son said, "Boy, take my ad-vice, Just fol-low pa-pa's foot-steps and you'll al-ways have the price. You've got to be real fly, my lad, to gain pros-per-i-ty; So do your neigh-bor and your friend, it's busi-ness, child," said he: Yes, do, do, my huc-kle-ber-ry do be care-ful what you do, do. Just try and be a Mas-cot, not a Jo-nah or a Hoo-doo, You do, do, do, my huc-kle-ber-ry, do, they'd do you if they could, So when you do your neigh-bors, don't for-get to do them good.

Ah, love is such a simple thing, some think it quite absurd,
But I've been loved by many girls, if I would take their word.
It's more a study than a gift, especially with our race;
They tell you that they love you, but of course it is a case

Chorus: Of do, do my huckleberry, do, the girls are far from true, do,
They call you sweet and tender names, their object is to hoodoo,
You do, do, do, my huckleberry, do, say nothing, but saw wood,
And when you do your people, don't forget to do them good.

A friend of mine he loaned me ten to pay my railroad fare,
Of course I took his home address, and said I'd send it there.
To-day there came a message, saying five of it would do;
And thinking he was crazy, why this answer back it flew:

Chorus: Oh! do, do, my huckleberry, do you say that five would do do?
I know you are a friend of mine, now tell me wouldn't two do?
You do, do, do, my huckleberry, do, I'd do you if I could,
For when I do my best friend, you can bet I do him good.

THE BOWERY

Charles Hoyt's "Trip to Chinatown" made the Bowery famous, both as a street and as a song. In the early 'Nineties this ribald account of night life in New York was considered just too devilish for words, and it travelled all over the country as the brightest and best of jokes on the much-abused son of the soil. (Incidentally, it killed the Bowery as a real estate proposition.)

The melody is very similar to that of the Neapolitan street song, *Spagnola*, which has also had its turn on the American hand-organs. The publisher was the house of Harms, later identified with some of the greatest musical comedy successes.

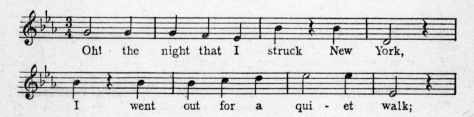

Oh! the night that I struck New York,
I went out for a qui-et walk;

Folks who are "on to" the ci-ty say,

Bet-ter by far that I took Broad-way;[1]

But I was out to en-joy the sights,

There was the Bow-'ry a-blaze with lights;

I— had one of the dev-il's own nights! I'll

nev-er go there a-ny more.

The Bow-'ry, the Bow-'ry! They say such

things, and they do strange[2] things on the Bow-'ry! The

Bow-'ry! I'll nev-er go there a-ny more!

I had walked but a block or two when up came a fellow and me he knew,[3]
Then a policeman came walking by, chased him away, and I asked him why,
"Wasn't he pulling your leg?" said he.   Said I: "He never laid hands on me!"[4]
"Get off the Bowery, you Yap!"[5] said he—I'll never go there any more.   [Chorus]

---

[1]Broadway, being a quiet and rather dull thoroughfare, naturally did not offer the manifold attractions of the East Side's Great White Way.

[2]The average singer usually repeated "such" in place of "strange."

[3]Of course he didn't really.

[4]Ignorant of slang, the crude fellow was taking the expression "pulling your leg" literally, ha, ha.

[5]One of the harshest names in any language, including the Scandinavian.

I went into an auction store. I never saw any thieves before.
First he sold me a pair of socks, then said he: "How much for the box?"
Someone said: "Two dollars!" I said: "Three!" He emptied the box and
   gave it to me—[6]
"I sold the box, not the socks," said he—I'll never go there any more. [Chorus]

I went into a concert hall, I didn't have a good time at all.
Just the minute that I sat down girls began singing, "New Coon in Town."[7]
I got up mad and spoke out free. "Somebody put that man out," said she.
A man called a bouncer attended to me—I'll never go there any more! [Chorus]

I went into a barber shop, he talked till I thought he would never stop;[8]
I cut it short, he misunderstood, clipped down my hair just as close as he could;
He shaved with a razor that scratched like a pin, took off my whiskers and most
   of my chin;
That was the worst scrape[9] I ever got in—I'll never go there any more. [Chorus]

I struck a place that they called a "dive," I was in luck to get out alive.
When the policeman heard my woes, saw my black eyes and my battered nose,
"You've been held up," said the "copper" fly! "No, sir but I've been knock'd
   down," said I;[10]
Then he laughed, though I couldn't see why—I'll never go there any more.
   [Chorus]

(Copyright, 1892, by T. B. Harms & Co. Used by permission.)

[6]Only a very stupid yokel would have permitted such a trick.

[7]He should not have resented this. It was his own fault if he got bounced.

[8]The talkative barber joke was already well established in 1892. In fact, it dates back to early
Roman history.

[9]This is really a delicious play on words. It was the barber who was scraping him, of course.

[10]A real climax of wit. Even to-day it is not generally known that to be "held up" means to be
robbed. Under the circumstances, the laughter of the "fly copper" was a bit cruel.

AFTER THE BALL, THE DELUGE

The first song to "sweep the country," the first "smashing, sensational success" of modern times was unquestionably *After the Ball*, by Charles K. Harris. The composer has told its story in a delightful autobiography of the same title,[1] and a careful reading of this book should convince any one of Mr. Harris's significance in the musical history of the world.

[1]"After the Ball—Forty Years of Melody," by Charles K. Harris, Frank-Maurice, Inc., N. Y.,
1926.

It will be easier to discuss this classic of the early 'Nineties after you have at least read the words, and perhaps sung it through; so here it is, in bald outline:

A lit-tle maid-en climbed an old man's knee,__

Begged for a sto-ry, "Do Un-cle please!__ Why

are you sin-gle; Why live a-lone?__ Have you no

ba-bies, have you no home?"__ "I had a sweet-

heart, years, years a-go;__ Where she is now pet, you

will soon know;__ List to the sto-ry, I'll tell it

all,__ I be-liev'd her faith-less, af-ter the ball."__

Af-ter the ball is ov-er, Af-ter the break of morn.__

Af-ter the dan-cers' leav-ing; Af-ter the stars are gone;__

Ma-ny a heart is ach-ing, If you could read them all;__

Ma-ny the hopes that have van-ish'd Af-ter the ball.__

Bright lights were flashing in the grand ballroom,
Softly the music, playing sweet tunes,
There came my sweetheart, my love, my own,
"I wish some water; leave me alone."
When I returned, dear, there stood a man,
Kissing my sweetheart as lovers can.
Down fell the glass-pet, broken, that's all,
Just as my heart was, after the ball. [*Chorus*]

Long years have passed, child, I've never wed,
True to my lost love, though she is dead,
She tried to tell me, tried to explain,
I would not listen, pleadings were vain.
One day a letter came from that man,
He was her brother, the letter ran,
That's why I'm lonely, no home at all,
I broke her heart, pet, after the ball. [*Chorus*]

It is difficult to decide to-day why this combination of words and music should so completely have upset the equilibrium of singing America nearly thirty-five years ago. Certainly, it is not an easy song to perform. The key of the chorus is much too high, and if it is transposed lower, then the verse becomes uncomfortably close to a bass range. (In playing *After the Ball*, the writer generally switches to the key of F for the chorus, thus keeping the whole thing within reach of the average voice, including his own. That makes the chorus begin on A, with D for a top note.)

But the fact remains that practically everybody sang it. J. Aldrich Libby, the baritone who introduced it (his pictures make him look like Andy Gump, but he must have had a wonderful voice) actually sang *After the Ball* half a tone higher than it was written.

Mr. Harris himself vividly tells the story of the first performance, at a matinée of Hoyt's "Trip to Chinatown," in Milwaukee's Bijou Theatre. He had persuaded the great Libby to give his song a trial, and Frank Palma, leader of the orchestra, had made a special orchestration, for the price of a cigar, as the composer was literally broke. He stood in the aisle by the wall, with Eddie Dillon, a young reporter:

Then came the Chinatown scene, in the second act, in which Libby walked out to the footlights in full evening dress. The orchestra commenced playing the introduction to the song, and then Libby, in his magnificent, clear, high baritone voice, sang the first verse and chorus. When he finished not a sound was heard. I was ready to sink through the floor. He then went through the second verse and the chorus, and again complete silence reigned. I was making ready to bolt, but my friend Dillon held me tightly by the arm. Then came the third verse and chorus. For a full minute the audience remained quiet, and then broke loose with applause.

After all these years, that matinée stands vividly fixed in my memory. The entire audience arose and, standing, wildly applauded for fully five minutes.

Libby's entire supporting company, including Julius Witmark, Laura Biggar, and Harry Connors[1], emerged from the wings and also applauded the singer in full view of the audience. Libby was compelled to sing the chorus at least six times over. When the audience had filed out after the performance the players pleaded with Frank Palma to hold the orchestra for a repetition of the instrumentation.

Witmark was ready to offer $10,000 immediately for the complete rights to the song, but Harris wisely declined. When a postal card, dated April 1st, came from the Oliver Ditson Company of Boston, ordering 75,000 copies for immediate delivery, the composer thought it was an April-fool joke and tore it up. Ten days later a wire came from the same firm, "Have you shipped the order for *After the Ball*? When and where? Answer immediately." "Then," says Mr. Harris, "it dawned upon me that the postcard was not a joke, but a bona-fide order."

This huge hit became well established when John Philip Sousa played it constantly at the World's Fair in Chicago. Later the people of the Middle West sang a parody:

> After the Fair is over, what will Chicago do
> With all those empty houses, run up with sticks and glue?
> I'd rather live in Brooklyn (somebody'd know me there)
> Than to live in Chicago, after the Fair.[2]

----

[1] The name should be Conor.

[2] The Chicago World's Fair made musical history in a variety of ways. It was the Midway that inspired *The Streets of Cairo*, which introduced the ultra-naughty "hoochee-coochee" to America. For years after that, little boys on the streets could be heard singing "Oh, what a funny feeling, Stepped on a banana peeling," etc.

The St. Louis Exposition produced one really popular song, *Meet me at Saint Looey, Looey, Meet me at the Fair*, but Chicago had several, while the Sesqui has been musically inarticulate up to the time of writing.

In fact, there were many parodies of *After the Ball*, the surest indications in those days of a song's popularity. The best known, perhaps, is the one about the largely false lady:

> After the ball is over, Mary takes out her glass eye,
> Puts her false teeth in cold water, corks up her bottle of dye,
> Throws her cork leg in a corner, hangs up her wig on the wall,
> Then what, is left goes to by-low, after the ball.

(There was also a current vaudeville joke in which one performer asked another why he was whistling. The answer was, "I have lost my ball." "And what are you whistling?" was the next question. "I am whistling *After the Ball*," was the logical response.)

Like most of the great successes of the past century, *After the Ball* had its foundation in reality.

"As a young man," writes Mr. Harris, "I had often attended balls, social soireés and the like," so what more natural than that he should go with his sister to a ball in Chicago? There he met the "dark-eyed Southern girl" who eventually became his wife. But that is not the story.

Gathered in our group that night was a charming young couple, engaged to be married. Suddenly we learned that the engagement was broken. Just a lovers' quarrel, I presumed at the time; but they were both too proud to acknowledge that they were in the wrong.

The ball lasted until early in the morning, and we were all leaving for our respective homes, when I noticed, just ahead of our party, waiting for his carriage, this young man escorting, not his fiancée, but another charming miss. Lover-like, he probably felt that, by causing his sweetheart a pang of jealousy, she would be more willing to forgive and forget. Of course, she did not know this. She simply knew that her Harry was easily consoled and that her place was usurped by another. Tears came to her eyes, though she tried to hide them behind a smile and a careless toss of the head. On witnessing this little drama the thought came to me like a flash, "Many a heart is aching after the ball," and this was the inception of that well-known song.

The next day Mr. Harris was resting, "completely exhausted," in his studio, when Sam Doctor, a tailor and an amateur singer, came in to ask him to compose a special song for the minstrel show of the Wheelmen's Club at the Academy of Music. The scene of the previous evening came back to him like a flash, and in an hour's time the whole of *After the Ball* had been written.

Doctor's performance of the song, however, proved a fiasco, as he forgot his words at the beginning of the third verse, and had to sit down without finishing it, leaving the plot unexplained, after which the composer made the resolution: "Never again shall an amateur singer introduce any new song of mine," and he has kept that resolution to this day.

The original manuscript of *After the Ball*, of which there is a fac-simile in the Harris Autobiography, shows that, like Beethoven, this composer was not satisfied with a first draft. "Babies" was written in, where "sweetheart" first stood, and several tentative lines in the first verse were eliminated:

> Tears slowly falling (?) down on his cheek,
> Clasping the dear child, arms trembling weak,
> I'll tell a story, yes, tell you all,
> Life lost its sunshine after the ball.

Similarly the second verse lost the lines:

> Merry the dancers, happy were they,
> No thoughts of sorrow darkens their way.
>
> . . . .
>
> Quickly I hastened, happy was I,
> Sweet precious moments, when she was nigh.

The third verse also was originally a bit more specific:

> After the ball, pet, on our way home,
> Not a word spoken as though alone.
>
> . . . .
>
> Then came a letter from that same man, etc.

Harris's idea of having a child drag the story out of its uncle was entirely his own. It also gave him a chance to use the word "pet" practically as a suffix, whenever an extra syllable was needed, so much so that on one or two occasions (as above) it appears hy-phenated with the preceding word.

The text contains some splendid specimens of assonance, and the accenting of both definite and indefinite articles should be of the greatest interest to serious students of prosody. It has never been explained why the girl did not say, simply, "Meet my brother,

Charlie." But in that case, of course, there would have been no song.

Break the News to Mother, which probably stands second in the affections of Mr. Harris's public, arose from a line in William Gillette's starring vehicle, "Secret Service." A wounded drummer-boy was brought to his home and said to the darky at the door "Break the news to Mother."

"C. K." wrote the line down on his cuff the moment he heard it, but it was in a barber's chair that the final punch of his song occurred to him. "I'm going to kill him!" he suddenly shouted, and so indeed it proved.

This song had to wait for a war to make it popular, and the little misunderstanding with Spain was providential. Even though the text referred to "the boys in blue," it filled the bill, and the whole country was soon singing it.

Here is the authentic version of *Break the News to Mother:*

While the shot and shell were scream-ing up-on the bat-tle field; The boys in blue were fight-ing their no-ble flag to shield; Came a cry from their brave cap-tain, "Look, boys! our flag is down; Who'll vol-un-teer to save it from dis-grace?" "I will" a young voice shout-ed, "I'll bring it back, or die;" Then sprang in-to the thick-est of the fray; Saved the flag but gave his young life; all for his coun-try's sake. They

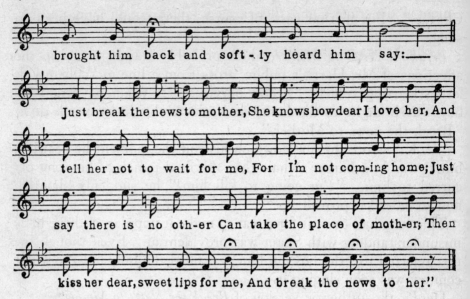

brought him back and soft - ly heard him say:___

Just break the news to mother, She knows how dear I love her, And

tell her not to wait for me, For I'm not com-ing home; Just

say there is no oth-er Can take the place of moth-er; Then

kiss her dear, sweet lips for me, And break the news to her."

From afar a noted general had witnessed this brave deed.
"Who saved our flag? Speak up lads; 'twas noble, brave, indeed!"
"There he lies, sir," said the captain, "he's sinking very fast,"
Then slowly turned away to hide a tear.
The general, in a moment, knelt down beside the boy;
Then gave a cry that touch'd all hearts that day.
"It's my son, my brave, young hero; I thought you safe at home."
"Forgive me, Father, for I ran away." [*Chorus*]

Charles K. Harris was responsible for a number of other hits, and is still active on Broadway, with his interest turning largely toward motion pictures of his famous titles. He has two highly successful "kid songs" to his credit, *Always in the Way* and *Kiss and Let's Make Up*. *Hello, Central, Give Me Heaven* was the first of a long line of telephone songs, with a direct descendant in Al Jolson's *Hello, Central, Give Me No Man's Land*.

Better than Gold, a popular moralizer, opened with the lines:

In a Pullman palace smoker sat a number of bright men.
You could tell that they were drummers; nothing seemed to trouble them.

They decide to have "three wishes," at the suggestion of "a bright knight of the grip." One man says, "Your attention for a moment I do crave," and then argues in favour of enough gold to keep the wolf from the door.

This brings on the climax:

> The conductor passing through the train, stopped in the smoking-car.
> He had grown quite interested in the stories told so far.

His wish, of course, is for something better than gold, namely "my baby, wife, and home." This song was introduced with slides representing actual photographs of the new fast train between Chicago and Minneapolis, a wonderful achievement at that time.

But the feat of writing an entire song in dialogue was reserved for *There'll Come a Time*, a splendid piece of moralizing, which is to-day classed by many, unconsciously, as part of the hymnology of the world. With an absolute command of his technique, Mr. Harris tells his whole story without once resorting to even a "he said" or "replied the tot."

While the chorus is quite familiar, you may have forgotten the verses, and this will remind you of one of virtue's choicest ornaments:

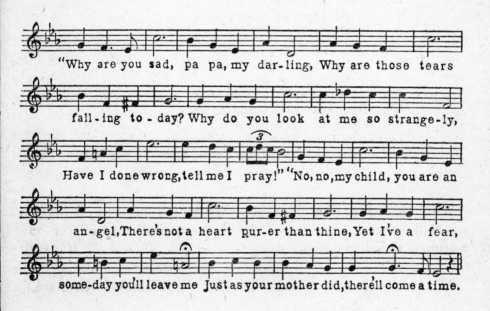

"Why are you sad, pa pa, my dar-ling, Why are those tears fall-ing to - day? Why do you look at me so strange-ly, Have I done wrong, tell me I pray!" "No, no, my child, you are an an-gel, There's not a heart pur-er than thine, Yet I've a fear, some-day you'll leave me Just as your mother did, there'll come a time.

There'll come a time, some day,___ When I have passed a-
way,___ There'll be no fath-er to guide you
from day to day,___ Think well of all I've
said;___ Hon-or the man you wed;___ Al-ways re-
mem-ber my sto-ry, there'll come a time."___

"Let me know all, papa, my darling,
Tell me I pray, of mother dear,
Where has she gone, why did she leave us,
Why is her name never heard here?
I never felt her arms about me,
Nor her sweet lips prest close to mine,
I'd give my life, only to see her.
Tell me, dear papa, will there come a time?" [*Chorus*]

"Some years ago, well I remember,
Your mother, child, left home one night,
She fled alas, fled with another,
'Tis the old tale, vanished from sight,
'Twas but a year, back to the old home,
She came to die, yes, baby mine.
That's why I fear, some day you'll leave me,
Just as your mother did, there'll come a time." [*Chorus*]

What this editor likes best about Mr. Harris, however, is that he
was willing to publish one of the greatest of all take-offs on the
sentimental ballads of his day, *Heaven Will Protect the Working
Girl.*

This was written for Marie Dressler, in "Tillie's Nightmare," by A. Baldwin Sloane, with words by Edgar Smith. The copyright was renewed in 1937 by Mae Sloane, widow of the composer, and is now jointly controlled by the Charles K. Harris Music Publishing Company and the Jerry Vogel Music Company, Inc.

It is a curious but undeniable fact that many people today consider *Heaven Will Protect the Working Girl* a bona fide tear-jerker of the Gay Nineties or earlier, even though its burlesque spirit seems entirely obvious. The song was introduced in all seriousness in the Theatre Guild's cavalcade of American music, *Sing Out, Sweet Land!*, in which Alfred Drake, Burl Ives and Bibi Osterwald exuded such masses of nostalgic charm. Actually it had no place in such a show, even as a parody.

Comedians are inclined to point the humor of such a song more heavily than even its creators could have intended, and this habit has unfortunately spread also to the interpretation of the legitimate ballads of our maudlin past. It is quite unnecessary to emphasize the absurdity of such material; a straight-faced delivery, as though believing every word and taking it as a matter of course, is far more effective. Singers who indulge in falsetto squeaks and yodels, with other distortions of a perfectly conventional melody line, are merely spoiling something that in itself is funny enough and often sentimentally appealing as well.

Parody as a Compliment

The fact that a song or a definite style of composition is parodied should be considered the highest tribute, for nothing can win that honor without first establishing a sufficiently wide popularity to make the parody obvious to the average listener. The danger of parody, of course, is that some people can always be found who will take it seriously. The dividing line between the blunt or implied statement that "this is just kidding" and the subtle insinuation of the same purpose is often very faint. It takes an artist to do it really well.

When Mr. Sloane wrote such phrases as "I hope you won't forget that I'm the only mother you have got" and the oft quoted classic, "You may tempt the upper classes with your villainous demitasses," he certainly left no room for doubt as to his intentions.

TWO LITTLE GIRLS IN BLUE

Unquestionably inspired by the success of *After the Ball*, this was the big hit of Charles Graham, who was responsible also for a number of other popular songs.[1]   The technique of *Two Little Girls in Blue* is precisely the same as that of the C. K. Harris humdinger, and incidentally both songs were featured by the same portentous J. Aldrich Libby.   (Mr. Graham adds an E to his name, which may or may not be an improvement.)

In both cases the story is told by one generation to another. The little girl who climbs upon the avuncular knee in *After the Ball* becomes a nephew in *Two Little Girls in Blue*, and the suffix "pet," used so effectively as a stop-gap by Mr. Harris, has its parallel in the "lad" of the Graham song.

The doleful uncle is consistently asked to explain his sadness, and in each case the answer reveals a misunderstanding.   But Mr. Harris's regretter gave up his girl on the strength of seeing her kissed by her brother at a party, while the narrator of *Two Little Girls in Blue* progressed as far as marriage and then "thought her unfaithful."   "We quarrelled, lad, and parted that night for life."   In the latter case, we are not told how the mistake occurred, merely that

> My fancy of jealousy wronged a heart,
> A heart that was good and true,
> For two better girls never lived than they,
> Those two little girls in blue.

Here is Mr. Graham's chorus:

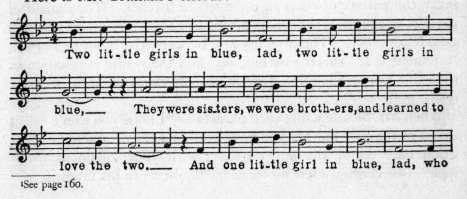

Two lit-tle girls in blue, lad, two lit-tle girls in blue,___ They were sis-ters, we were broth-ers, and learned to love the two.___ And one lit-tle girl in blue, lad, who

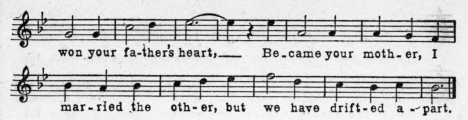

won your fa-ther's heart,___ Be.came your moth.er, I

mar-ried the oth-er, but we have drift-ed a -part.

(*Copyright, 1893, by Spaulding & Kornder, assigned to M. D. Swisher, Used by permission.*)

WITH ALL HER FAULTS I LOVE HER STILL

A gentleman named Monroe H. Rosenfeld, who wrote for the newspapers and had apparently unlimited capacities of various kinds, was responsible for several of the gems of lyric sentimentality that appeared during the 'Nineties. Here is one of his titles which has become an accepted phrase in the American language. The song does not specify the exact faults that the bereft lover had in mind, and this is a bit of an oversight on the part of the journalist author and composer. The fact that she left the self-appointed hero should be counted in her favour, if at all.

The very musical arrangement in which this ballad appears to-day is credited to "D. Onivas," who is none other than Domenico Savino (backwards), one of the masters of modern jazz orchestration. The melody itself belongs to the "echo school," in which a solo line can be repeated in barber-shop harmonies. Compare *Sweet Adeline* and its unintentional ancestor, *Say Au Revoir but not Good-bye*, as well as the perennially plaintive *How Dry I Am*. (See also *We Never Speak as We Pass by*, p. 61.) The final note can be sung an octave higher if the interpreter is overcome by his emotions.

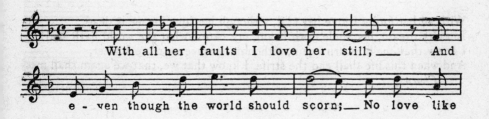

With all her faults I love her still, ___ And

e - ven though the world should scorn;___ No love like

hers, my heart can thrill, Al-though she's made that heart for-

lorn! Tho' oth-er hearts have won her love, I bear for

her no dreams of ill, Her face to me still dear shall

be, With all her faults I love, I love her still!

With al her faults I love her still,——And e-ven so till Death doth

part!——No love like hers, my soul can thrill—— No

oth-er love can win my heart! I love her still! I love her

still,—— With all her faults I love her still.——

She went away one summer day, and never came again to me,
And since that day I long and pray that I may pass Life's dreary sea!
I see her now as first we met, the sunlight shining o'er her brow,
The days were joy without alloy, but ah! my heart, my heart is weary now!
    [*Chorus*]

With all her faults I love her still, although her love for me is dead,
In ev'ry dream, her smile doth beam, nor care I what the world hath said!
I know that she'll return again, although her face no more I greet,
And when this life shall end the strife, I know that we, that we again shall meet!
    [*Chorus*]

TAKE BACK YOUR GOLD

This song, which was selected for the revival of "East Lynne" as completely characteristic of its period, represents Monroe H. Rosenfeld at his wickedest. The words are by a certain Louis W. Pritzkow.

The mere quotation of the text and tune should be sufficient recommendation, and no comment is required. There is a lack of finality about the plot which is disappointing. One wants to know whether she persisted in refusing his financial aid, whether he actually married another girl, and what the jilted one did about it, if anything.

Historically, *Take Back Your Gold* is significant as the vehicle for the stage entrance of Emma Carus. The famous "lady baritone" had been throwing her voice chiefly across the counter of Petrie, the publisher, and as the latter was in the habit of trying out his clerks occasionally as song-pluggers, he gave Emma a chance in Boston, evidently figuring that her masculine tones would give just the proper melodramatic value to this song.

She never came back.

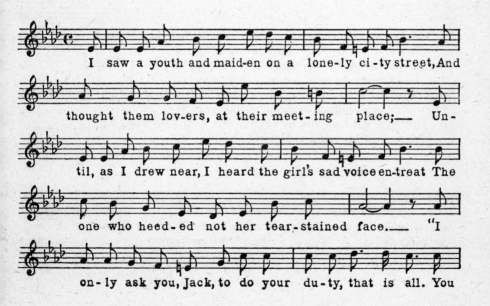

know you prom-ised that we should be wed." And

when he said, "You shall not want, what-ev-er may be-fall," She

spurned the gold he of-fered her and said:___

"Take back your gold, for gold can nev-er buy me;

Take back your bribe, and prom-ise you'll be true;

Give me the love, the love that you'd de-ny me;

Make me your wife, that's all I ask of you."[1]

He drew her close unto him and to soothe her then he tried,
But she in pride and sorrow turned away,
And as he sought to comfort her, she wept and softly sighed,
"You'll rue your cruel actions, Jack, some day."[2]
"Now, little one, don't cry," he said, "for though to-night we part,
And though another soon will be my bride,[3]
This gold will help you to forget," but with a breaking heart,
She scorned his gift and bitterly replied: [Chorus]

---

[1]And a very modest request, when all is said and done.
[2]The succession of oo vowels in this sentence creates an effect of great pathos.
[3]Ay, there's the rub.   He should have mentioned this much earlier.

GOLD WILL BUY 'MOST ANYTHING BUT A TRUE GIRL'S HEART

This is one of the most convincing utterances on an all-absorbing topic in American song literature. The picture, however, which appeared on the original title-page, does not make it clear just why the gentleman preferred the non-wealthy girl, in spite of her up-to-date bob and undeniable sincerity. Rosenfeld is again responsible and again the outcome of the story remains veiled in mystery. We can only hope that the good girl stuck to her resolution.

A poor girl stood one evening with-in her humble dwelling And
lis-tened, while a rich girl to her said:— "I've
learned that you're to marry the one I've loved since childhood, The
man whom but for you I should have wed![1]__ See
here are gold and jewels rare, gems a queen would glad-ly wear, What
need you care for him— the world is wide!__ Come,
say you'll give him up to me, And half my for-tune yours shall be! But
plead - ing - ly the loy - al girl re - plied:

[1] A masterly bit of English, that will stand firm against every grammarian's attack.

"Do not try to tempt me, Miss, I can-not grant your plea,—My
love for Jack is faith-ful— and he, I know, loves me;— So
all your wealth and je-wels rare can nev-er make us part,—
Gold will buy most an-y-thing but a true girl's heart."—

"Don't think that you can tempt me, for tho' I'm poor and lowly,
I'd rather have my Jack than all your gold;[2]
The world is ruled by riches, but one thing, Miss, remember
A love like mine can ne'er be bought or sold!"
The child of wealth turned to the door but she stopped to say once more:
"Don't be a fool, another you can wed!
Don't turn away, do say you will,
My fortune, see, I offer still,"
But with a flashing eye the poor girl said: [*Chorus*]

(Copyright, 1898, by Howley Haviland & Co., assigned to Pioneer Music Pub. Co. Used by permission.)

JUST FOR THE SAKE OF OUR DAUGHTER

An 1897 model from the Monroe H. Rosenfeld factory. The
original cover design gave a vivid pictorial summary of the plot,
with Joe Howard, of vaudeville fame, posing as the half-shot
burglar, while the wronged husband was obviously a policeman.

---

[2]Modern slang has made an unfortunate pun out of this line, which the original author would have
repudiated as unworthy. The irreverent modernist is almost sure to argue that she could have had
her jack and spent it too.

On the back of this song several gems are suggested, to be "tried on your piano," all by the
same prolific Mr. Rosenfeld. One chorus begins:

"She was happy till she met you,
And the fault is all your own.
If she wishes to forget you,
You will please leave her alone."

Two other titles are *I Was Once Your Wife* and *Don't Ask Me to Give up My Mother*, both reason-
able enough.

There was so much action to this song that the mere verse-chorus form would have been insufficient, and the actual music goes through elaborate operatic effects, with recitative, etc. Why not compose your own version?

A white-robed little maid, one night, was creeping into bed,
And as she knelt to lisp her prayers her father gently said:
"To-night I want you, little one, to say while I am here
A prayer for her who's coming back, I mean your mother dear."
The little child looked up surprised and said, "Why, Dad, you know
I haven't any mamma, for you told me long ago
That she was dead and gone away so far from you and I,[1]
How can she now come home to us?" but he made no reply.

> Chorus: Just for the sake of his[2] daughter,
>   Just for the sake of his[2] child,
> Just for the sake of her innocence,
>   So pure and undefiled;
> Just for the sake of the blighted past,
>   The past that now is reconciled;
> Just for the sake of the one he loved[3] best,
>   For the sake of his[2] little baby child.

The little maiden knelt in prayer, then rose and said: "Why, Dad,
If Mamma's coming home to us, what makes you look so sad?"
And as in haste he sought to brush the falling tears away,
He sighed, "Perhaps your mother, child, will tell you all some day."
The little one lay sleeping when the erring wife returned,
Returned to seek again the trusting love that she had spurned;
And as she said, "I'm sorry, John"[4] he kissed her careworn face,
And murmured, "I forgive you, Jane, my home's your resting place."

The husband sat in silence, while his wife and baby slept,
As thro' an open window the form of a burglar crept.
"Who's that?" the father cried; and as they meet in deadly strife,[5]
The light reveals the traitor who had lured away his wife.
"My God! I've found you, wretch, at last, your day has come! Now stand!"
A pistol shot, a leap, a scream, and then a woman's hand
Held back the smoking weapon, as a voice cried, "Spare his life,
For her sake and for my sake, John, For your own wretched wife!"

---

[1]For an earlier use of this Lardnerian locution, see *Allie Darling*, by Rutledge and Danks, p. 669.

[2]Second chorus "your"; third chorus, "our."

[3]Second chorus "you love"; third chorus "we love."

[4]Well, she apologized, so what was there to do?

[5]Here the accompaniment becomes agitato, in movie style, while the voice dramatically declaims the words.

DON'T SAY I DID IT, JACK, *or* FOR HER GOOD NAME

The chorus of this song is musically the legitimate parent of *Good-bye, My Bluebell*. Its fine spirit of chivalry and disregard of accepted conventions should make a strong appeal to modern readers of the tabloid newspapers. It is a Rosenfeld production.

It was near the hour of midnight,
While walking down the street,
Two men upon their homeward way
A comrade chanced to meet.
To him they'd long been strangers,
And so, unrecognized,
They sought to turn away from him
Whose friendship they despised.
Said he in drunken accents,
"Tom, I've just left little May,
We had a jolly time, old man,
You know she's light and gay"—
"Liar!" cried the brother;[1]
Then a shot rang thro' the air,
As to his friend he muttered,
While the lifeless form lay there:

Chorus: "Don't say I did it, Jack,
Don't let them know,
Don't tell my sister that for her I struck the blow,
He was to blame, you see,
You'd have done the same;
I had to do it, Jack, for her good name."

"I'm no coward, Jack, you know it,
So what was I to do?
I could not hear her slandered,
For she is so good and true."
"That's so!" his comrade answered,
"It was the only way,[2]
And I, too, always loved her, Tom,
She'll be my wife some day;

---

[1] The dramatic agitato chords in the accompaniment strike a new note in popular song-writing and are the forerunners of the whole school of musical realism in the motion-picture theatres.
[2] Obviously.

For surely in the great **Beyond,**
'Twill be adjudged no crime,
A woman's honor to defend,
E'en to the end of time."
"Bless you!" cried the brother,
"When to little May you're wed,[3]
You'll sometimes think of me, Jack,[4]
And remember what I said:[5] [*Chorus*]

AND HER GOLDEN HAIR WAS HANGING DOWN HER BACK

Monroe Rosenfeld occasionally lent his creative inspiration to comedy, and this is one of the few cases in which he deliberately deserted the traditional ballad style. The rather cynical words, however, were written for him by Felix McGlennon.

There was once a simple maiden came to New York on a trip,
And her golden hair was hanging down her back.
Her cheeks were like the roses, she'd a pout upon her lip,
And her golden hair was hanging down her back.
When she landed at the station here she took a little stroll,
At ev'rything she wondered till she lost her self-control,
Said she, "New York is quite a village, ain't it? Bless my soul!"
And her golden hair was hanging down her back.

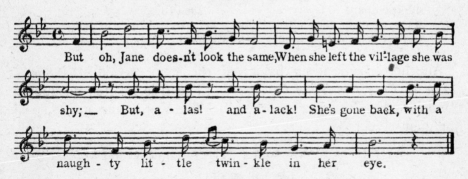

But oh, Jane does-n't look the same, When she left the vil-lage she was shy;— But, a-las! and a-lack! She's gone back, with a naugh-ty lit-tle twin-kle in her eye.

[3]The consistent use of head-line English in this song suggests its enormous journalistic possibilities. False Friend Shot in Drunken Brawl; Will Wed Slayer's Good True Sister; Jack Backs Tom Defending Little May;—these are only a few hints for the copy-desk.

[4]This line indicates that Tom expects to pay the penalty, although he seems fully justified in having lost his temper.

[5]We are mercifully spared any further details of this tragic story. Probably the judge let Tom off with a reprimand, after Jack had moved the jury to tears with his confession.

I WON'T LET YOU INSULT HER

The words and music of this stirring song were written by Dave Augustine, and it was published by George L. Spaulding. It tells its own story quite adequately.

Three gentlemen were seated in a crowded smoking car,
They noticed on a bill-board the picture of a star,[1]
An actress fair to look upon and peerless in her art,
They said 'twas rumored that her charms had broken many a heart.
One spoke of her great beauty, another of her fame,
The last one said she'd fallen but perhaps was not to blame.
A gentleman who had been sitting in a seat close by,
Sprang to his seat[2] and loudly cried, "You coward, cur, you lie.

Chorus:
"I won't let you insult her, while I am standing near,
I'm sure that she's a stranger to everybody here,
I know that she is pure and good, on that I'll stake my life,
I won't let you insult her now for she was once my wife."

"Although you all are strange to me the tale I'll tell to you,
When first we wed I thought I could never be untrue,
But scarce a year had passed away, in shame I tell it now,
She found the man she loved so well had broken ev'ry vow.
She loved me so I think her poor heart broke on that sad day,
She tried hard to forgive me but she wished to go away.
'Twas then she went upon the stage her freedom there to gain,
And gentlemen I'd give my life to win her back again." [*Chorus*]

Another heartrending ballad of the same period was *She Is More to Be Pitied Than Censured*. (The title is often misquoted, "more to be pitied than scorned.") The words and music speak for themselves:

SHE IS MORE TO BE PITIED THAN CENSURED

At the old concert hall on the Bowery,
  'Round the table were seated one night
A crowd of young fellows carousing,
  With them life seemed cheerful and bright.

---

[1] Not a Macy advertisement. The reference is unquestionably to a bright light of the theatrical firmament.

[2] This is the original version, but "seat" is undoubtedly a misprint for "feet." Song literature is full of such little slips. It is hard to believe that the gentleman actually harangued the audience while standing on a seat, and of course there was no horse handy.

At the very next table was seated
A girl who had fallen to shame;
All the young fellows jeered at her weakness,
Till they heard an old woman exclaim:

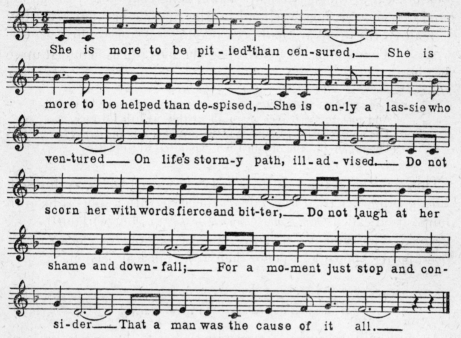

She is more to be pit-ied[1] than cen-sured,—— She is more to be helped than de-spised,——She is on-ly a las-sie who ven-tured—— On life's storm-y path, ill-ad-vised.—— Do not scorn her with words fierce and bit-ter,—— Do not laugh at her shame and down-fall;—— For a mo-ment just stop and con-si-der——That a man was the cause of it all.——

There's an old-fashioned church 'round the corner,
Where the neighbors all gathered one day.
While the parson was preaching a sermon
O'er a soul that had just passed away.
'Twas this same wayward girl from the Bow'ry,
Who a life of adventure had led—
Did the clergyman jeer at her downfall?
No—he asked for God's mercy, and said: [Chorus]

W. B. Gray, who published this song, wrote some popular successes on his own account, and was responsible for the words of *The Volunteer Organist*, which threatened for a time to create a new and permanent type of semi-religious lyricism.

The story was of a rural congregation in which the minister asked for someone to take the place of the absent organist, who was

---

[1] Pronounced "peeteed."

ill. There was a vivid description of the agitated looks that flew about the church, as all wondered who would volunteer, and then great excitement as a shabby drunkard staggered up the aisle and took his seat at the instrument. That congregation recognized the hand of a master, however, and by the time he had finished, they all realized the drunkard had been playing the story of his own life, no less! The impression made upon the narrator is summed up in the chorus:

> The scene was one I'll ne'er forget as long as I may live,
> And just to see it o'er again all earthly wealth I'd give,
> The congregation all amazed, the preacher old and gray,
> The organ and the organist who volunteered to play.

This song gave the title to a play, produced by Gray himself, and the publisher tried to establish the style with a song of his own composition called *Old Jim's Christmas Hymn*, but without lasting success. The same W. B. Gray made a song of *The Picture on the Floor*, better known as a poem than in its musical version.

I'LL BE HOME TO-MORROW NIGHT

An unusually optimistic temperance song is this masterpiece of Joe Howard, a vaudeville favourite in his day. Charlie Case had this and similar songs in mind when he wrote his parodies only a few years later. The story is enhanced by the realistic picture which appeared on the original title-page.

A story I'm going to tell of a mother old and gray,
She had children dear to her, and one, a son who ran away,
　　Each night at her home there's a vacant chair, and she longs just to see her
　　　boy again,
But he's now a slave to drink, though he often stops to think
　　Of home and writes this tender loving strain:

> *Chorus:*
> I've just come home, mother, don't feel bad,
> 　I've led the wrong life, I know that you are sad.
> But I've thrown off my comrades, I'll try to do right
> 　And heed your gentle warning, so I'll be home to-morrow night.

One night he returns to his home his poor mother to surprise,
She had given up all hope, and often sits at home and cries,
  He meets some old comrades just passing by, and they tempt him with brimming glass in vain,
For he cries I'll drink no more, opens wide his cottage door,
  And greets his mother with this new refrain:

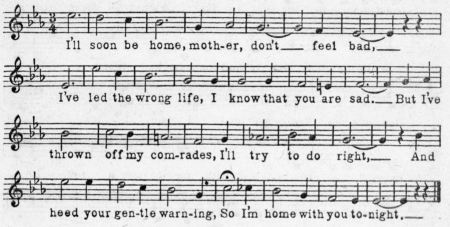

I'll soon be home, moth-er, don't___ feel bad,___
I've led the wrong life, I know that you are sad.___ But I've
thrown off my com-rades, I'll try to do right,___ And
heed your gen-tle warn-ing, So I'm home with you to-night.___

THE NEW BULLY

May Irwin, who now raises pedigreed cattle in the Thousand Islands (a big butter-and-egg woman), will always be remembered as the real mother of ragtime in America, and the song that did the trick was *The Bully*, to which the adjective "new" is still generally added.

The story goes that "The Country Sport" company, including Miss Irwin and Peter F. Dailey, were travelling from San Francisco to Chicago, and Charles E. Trevathan, a sports writer, was entertaining the Pullman passengers with some songs to the accompaniment of a guitar. A Negro melody which he had picked up in the South made such a hit that Miss Irwin insisted on his making a complete song out of it.

The Bully song was the result, and it went into the production of "The Widow Jones" the following season. The new and strange rhythm scored a knock-out first at Brockton, Mass., then in Boston, and finally at New York's Bijou Theatre.

Here is the complete song, as May Irwin sang it:

Have yo' heard a-bout dat bul-ly dat's just come to town? He's
round a-mong de nig-gers a - lay-in' their bod-ies down, I'm a-
look-in' for dat bul-ly and he must be found. I'm a
Ten-nes-see nig-ger and I don't al - low, No
red eyed riv-er roust-a-bout with me to raise a row. I'm
look-in' for dat bul-ly and I'll make him bow.
When I walk dat lev-ee round, round, round, round,
When I walk dat lev-ee round, round, round, round,
When I walk dat lev-ee round, I'm a-
look-in' for dat bul-ly an' he must be found.

I's gwine down the street with my ax in my hand,
I'm lookin' for dat bully and I'll sweep him off dis land,
I'm a-lookin' for dat bully and he must be found.
I'll take 'long my razor, I's gwine to carve him deep,
And when I see dat bully, I'll lay him down to sleep.
I'm lookin' for dat bully and he must be found. [Chorus]

I went to a wingin' down at Parson Jones,'
Took along my trusty blade to carve dat nigger's bones,
Just a lookin' for dat bully, to hear his groans.
I coonjined in the front door, the coons were prancing high,
For dat levee darky I skinned my foxy eye,
Just a-lookin' for dat bully but he wan't nigh.   [Chorus]

I asked Miss Pansy Blossom if she would wing a reel,
She says, "Law, Mr. Johnsing, how high you make me feel."
Then you ought to see me shake my sugar heel.
I was sandin' down the Mobile Buck just to cut a shine,
Some coon across my smeller swiped a watermelon rin',
I drawed my steel dat gemmen for to fin'.   [Chorus]

I riz up like a black cloud and took a look aroun',
There was dat new bully standin' on de ground.
"I've been lookin' for you nigger and I've got you found."
Razors 'gun a-flyin', niggers 'gun to squawk,
I lit upon dat bully just like a sparrow hawk,
And dat nigger was just a-dyin' to take a walk.   [Chorus]

When I got through with bully, a doctor and a nurse
Wan't no good to dat nigger, so dey put him in a hearse,
A cyclone couldn't have tore him up much worse.
You don't hear 'bout dat nigger dat treated folks so free,
Go down upon de levee, and his face you'll never see.
Dere's only one boss bully, an' dat one is me.   [Chorus]

Encore

When you see me comin' hist your windows high;
When you see me goin' hang your heads and cry;
I'm lookin' for dat bully and he must die.
My madness keeps a-risin' and I'se not gwine to get left,
I'm gettin' so bad dat I'm askeered of myself.
I was lookin' for dat bully, now he's on de shelf.   [Chorus]

Miss Irwin had another great "coon song" success in *Mamie, Come Kiss Your Honey Boy*, which was largely her own, as well as her *Frog Song, When You Ain't Got No Money, Well You Needn't Come Around* and *Mr. Johnson, Turn Me Loose* ("I got no money but a good excuse").

BARNEY FAGAN

Those who saw an old actor named Barney Fagan in "The Jazz Singer" may not have realized the full significance of this man. Forty years ago he was the greatest of all stage directors, with a genius for inventing new dance steps, and a miraculous eye for colour and light. Barney Fagan was the first man to use electric and calcium effects to their full advantage. But he was forty years ahead of his time. The minstrel shows of his day knew that he was extraordinarily gifted, but the public never fully discovered him. He was the director of all the elaborate acts for the Primrose and West minstrels, and later there was a troupe which bore his own name.

As a song-writer, Barney Fagan was responsible for several hits, including one of the greatest coon songs ever written, *My Gal is a High Born Lady*. This was one of the first slow fox-trots on record, and it took the country by storm. Here is the chorus:

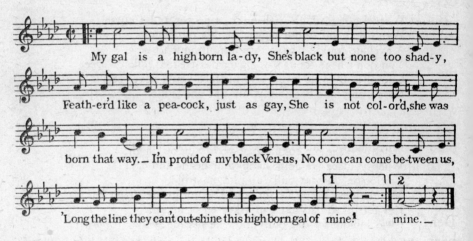

My gal is a high born la-dy, She's black but none too shad-y,
Feath-er'd like a pea-cock, just as gay, She is not col-or'd, she was
born that way.— I'm proud of my black Ven-us, No coon can come be-tween us,
'Long the line they can't out-shine this high born gal of mine.[1]　mine.—

The verses are interesting chiefly because nobody will remember ever having heard them before:

> Thar is gwine to be a festival this evenin',
> And a gatherin' of color mighty rare,

---

[1] Several variants of the words have been in common use, such as "not too shady," "she's so gay," "My gal, she is a Venus," "All the stars in Heav'n will shine on this," etc.

Thar'll be noted individuals of prominent distinctiveness,[2]
   To permeate the colored atmosphere.
Sunny Africa's Four Hundred's gwine to be thar,
   To do honor to my lovely fiancée,
Thar will be a grand ovation of especial ostentation,
   When the parson gives the dusky bride away. [*Chorus*]

When the preacher man propounds the vital question,
   "Does ye take the gal for better or for wuss?"[3]
I will feel as if my soul had left my body, gone to glory,
   And I know my heart will make an awful fuss.
I anticipates a very funny feelin',
   Nigger's eye-fall[4] like a diamond sure to shine,
But I'll bask in honeyed clover, when the ceremony's over,
   And I press the ruby lips of baby mine. [*Chorus*]

DECOLLETTE

Mr. Fagan's love of elegant language found an early expression in a song called *Decollette*, one of the most precious examples of society notes set to music. It was published by the Witmarks in 1893, and introduced by Julius Witmark himself, known first as "the boy soprano" (with medals) and later as a most successful baritone in the musical shows of his day. (See p. 160.)

Mr. Witmark, now the genial head of the famous publishers of the "Black and White Series" and other melody ballads, insists that Barney Fagan was quite aware that *Decollette* should rhyme with "say," but according to the printed words, it inevitably has the sound of "pet," which, incidentally, has always been the German pronunciation, and perhaps the Irish as well.

In any case, the song brings in a number of splendid French words, and the exact pronunciation doesn't matter very much. It is "respectfully dedicated to Miss Alice Black, Wilmington, Del.," who, nevertheless, can hardly be credited with having been the first lady of the land to wear a low-necked gown. It was only by accident that the Witmarks discovered a copy of this "Beautiful Song & Chorus (with Dance ad lib.):"

[2]Barney Fagan was noted for his command of English, and he liked to exercise his vocabulary, even in his songs. "Prominent distinctiveness," as Polonius would say, is "good," though perhaps redundant, and so is the "grand ovation of especial ostentation."

[3]The Negro dialect may be sketchy, but you get the idea.

[4]This is obviously a misprint. It should read either "Eye-full" or "eye-ball," probably the latter.

I have this mo-ment left a mas-quer-ade-ing par-ty, Of La

bal masque you must know I'm ver-y fond. But I par-tic-u-lar-ly go to see the

la - dies, And they were there the dash-ing bru-nette and the

blonde. With beau-ty style and grace I was be - wil-dered and it

placed me in a quand-'ry I con - fess, Glid-ing

through the ma-zy whirl I spied a lit-tle black-eyed girl in de-col-

lette the la - test fad in eve - ning dress

I lost my e - qui-lib-ri-um I was dazed my brain did

whirl My limbs be - came un - stead-y Gaz - ing

on this love-ly girl So ex - ceed-ing-ly fawn-like in

mo-tion, tin - y hands and dain-ty feet She was ev - 'ry

thing you could wish for and so de - sir - a - bly pe - tite.

Tho' there were ladies fair bedecked in regal splendor,
  Whose most charming manners one could bare resist,
To be gallant, I wished a service I dare render,
  But then my etiquette[1] compelled me to desist.
In dreamland I was passing through each measure,
  Side by side with one I fondly did caress;
It was she who tripped so light, was so demure and so polite,
  In decollette, the latest fad in evening dress.   [*Chorus*]

(*Copyright, 1893, by M. Witmark & Sons.   Used by permission.*)

HARRIS TO DRESSER TO VON TILZER

Paul Dresser, brother of Theodore Dreiser, the novelist, and one of the best-known and best-loved characters in the history of American song-writing, is remembered to-day chiefly by *The Banks of the Wabash*, which scorns the need of quotation.   But he wrote about fifty popular songs altogether, and several of these were palpable hits.   Among them were *Just Tell Them That You Saw Me*, *The Blue and the Gray*, *The Letter That Never Came*, *Here Lies an Actor*, *The Pardon Came too Late*, and *My Gal Sal*.

The Convict and the Bird is one of Dresser's earliest efforts, dating back to 1888.   Its subject matter has been popular with song-writers of all kinds, and public interest, with dogged persistency, still creates romance behind prison bars.

Paul Dresser, shortly after the publication of this song, organized the publishing firm of Howley, Haviland & Dresser, later Howley, Haviland & Co.   His death was untimely, and widely mourned, and his memory has been honoured by the State of Indiana with a monument on the banks of the Wabash.

THE CONVICT AND THE BIRD

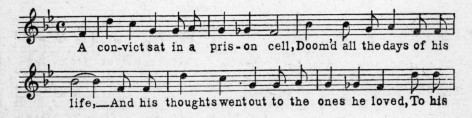

A con-vict sat in a pris-on cell, Doom'd all the days of his life,—And his thoughts went out to the ones he loved, To his

[1] Remember there were no books on this subject in 1893.

The bird he came to sing his song, At dusk on a summer's day.
And the poor thing chirped in loneliness, For no convict heard his lay,
He sang his notes so plaintively, Too sad for tongue to tell,
And at early morn, the faithful bird Lay dead in the convict's cell;
He sang no more of the sunshine, He sang no more of the clouds,
He sang no more of prosperity, Nor of poverty's sombre shrouds,
He sang no more of freedom, In the sky near the sun's bright ray,
And as he finished his song, The faithful bird it passed away.

Chorus: He came no more they say, He came no more each day,
        The messenger of freedom none could see,
        Silent was the cell, As if by magic spell,
        The convict like the bird again was free.

JUST TELL THEM THAT YOU SAW ME

Theodore Dreiser, who has left an intimate account of the composition of *The Banks of the Wabash* (mentioned also in some detail by Charles K. Harris in his memoirs), tells the personal story of his brother's second hit as well.   He conjectures that, like many other hits of the 'Nineties, *Just Tell Them That You Saw Me* was based upon some actual episode, and describes how Paul Dresser, on a gray November Sunday afternoon, began improvising at the piano, "or rather repeating over and over a certain strain which was evidently in his mind."

When Paul finally played the complete song for Theodore, he (Paul) broke down in the middle of the chorus, overcome with emotion.   Later the novelist was astonished at the song's sudden popularity and rapid sale.   "Some enterprising button firm got out a button on which the phrase was printed.   Comedians on the stage, newspaper paragraphers, his bank teller or his tailor, even staid business men wishing to appear up to date, used it as a parting salute."

There were the inevitable parodies also, one of which began:

> Just tell them that you saw me,
> But you didn't see me saw.

Just Tell Them That You Saw Me contains several priceless lines, notably, "'Is that you, Madge?'" I said to her, she quickly turned away, "'Don't turn away, Madge, I am still your friend'"; and "'Come home with me when I go, Madge, the change will do you good.'" Here is the chorus:

"Just tell them that you saw me," she said "they'll know the rest; Just tell them I was look-ing well you know. Just whisper if you get a chance to moth-er dear, and say, I love her as I did-long, long a - go."

The attractive feature of *The Blue and the Gray* is the chance to bring in *Dixie, Marching Through Georgia,* and *Yankee Doodle* as decorations during the chorus. The song would never have succeeded so long as it merely drew attention to the Civil War, but the sinking of the *Maine* created an immediate demand for martial music, and even though the uniforms did not fit, *The Blue and the Gray* had become a sensation by the time Dewey silenced the guns of Manila.

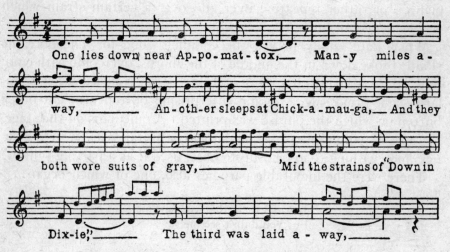

One lies down near Ap-po-mat-tox,— Man-y miles a-way,— An-oth-er sleeps at Chick-a-mau-ga,— And they both wore suits of gray,— 'Mid the strains of "Down in Dix-ie,"— The third was laid a - way,—

In a trench at Santiago, The Blue and the Gray.

Another popular Spanish War song was *Good-bye, Dolly Gray,*

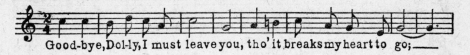

Good-bye, Dol-ly, I must leave you, tho' it breaks my heart to go;——

by Will Cobb and Paul Barnes, and later, when trouble developed in the Philippines, there was a sardonic song ending:

"I'd like to know who's a-running this show.
Is it me or Emilio Aguinaldo?"

A HOT TIME IN THE OLD TOWN

A Hot Time in the Old Town, however, is the tune indelibly associated with the Spanish War, for which it served very much as *Over There* and *The Long, Long Trail* did for the World War twenty years later. It is not generally remembered that this classic started out to be a camp-meeting ditty (although it lost its way after the first stanza), and in too many cases the chief recollection may be of some of the ribald parodies which ran wild among the rougher set for a time. The whole structure of this song is naïvely primitive. The verse part is merely the alternation of two very simple phrases; then comes the popular tune, acting both as the second half of the verse and as a chorus.

Theodore A. Metz wrote the music, and Joe Hayden the words, and the original publishers, in 1896, were Willis Woodward & Co.

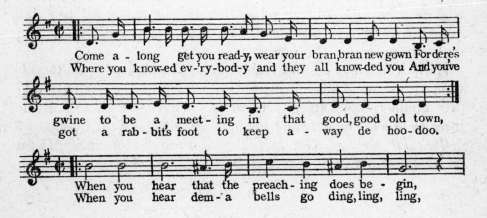

Come a - long   get you read-y, wear your bran, bran new gown For dere's
Where you know-ed ev-'ry-bod-y and they all know-ded you And you've

gwine   to be   a   meet - ing   in   that   good, good old town,
got   a rab - bit's foot   to keep   a - way   de   hoo- doo.

When you   hear   that the   preach - ing   does be - gin,
When you   hear   dem - a   bells   go   ding, ling,   ling,

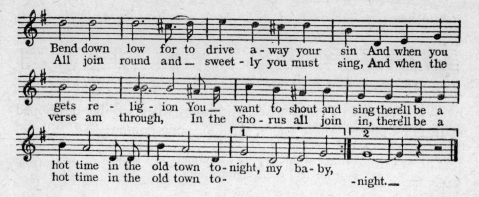

Bend down low for to drive a-way your sin And when you
All join round and— sweet-ly you must sing, And when the

gets re-lig-ion You— want to shout and sing there'll be a
verse am through, In the cho-rus all join in, there'll be a

hot time in the old town to-night, my ba-by,
hot time in the old town to-   -night.—

There was a second verse and chorus, as follows: .

> There'll be girls for ev'rybody in that good, good old town,
> For dere's Miss Consola Davis and dere's Miss Gondolia Brown,
> And dere's Miss Johanna Beasly,[1] she am dressed all in red,
> I just hugged her and I kissed her and to me then she said:
> Please, oh, please, oh, do not let me fall,
> You're all mine and I love you best of all,
> And you must be my man or I'll have no man at all,
> There'll be a hot time in the old town to-night, my baby.
> When you hear dem bells go ding, ling, ling, etc.

Harry von Tilzer's Hits

The triumvirate of old-timers, which started with Charles K. Harris and Paul Dresser, is logically completed by Harry Von Tilzer. He is probably the last of those natural creators of melody who exercised a species of hypnotism on the public of their day and seemed to have a genius for inevitably combining words and music in an irresistible appeal.

Harry Von Tilzer is still writing songs in his little office on Broadway, although he has turned out at least a dozen hits that sold over a million copies apiece. He claims to have written as many as three thousand songs before his first real success went over.

Wait Till the Sun Shines, Nellie, On a Sunday Afternoon, Down Where the Wurzburger Flows, A Bird in a Gilded Cage, All Alone,

---

[1]These ladies are mere names to-day, and probably were then.

Please Go 'Way and Let Me Sleep, I'd Leave Ma Happy Home for You, Good-bye, Eliza Jane, The Cubanola Glide, Alexander, What You Goin' to Do when the Rent Comes Round? I Want a Girl, Take Me Back to New York Town, Down on the Farm, My Old New Hampshire Home, On the Old Fall River Line—these are only a few of the "wows" that this one man produced, and in the greatest variety of styles.

The antiquarian of song literature is likely to sigh most affectionately over the *Bird in a Gilded Cage*, a title which has become a stock phrase, and which the composer calls "the key that opened the door of wealth and fame" for him.   Arthur J. Lamb, who wrote the lyrics of *Asleep in the Deep, The Bird on Nellie's Hat*, and other famous songs, brought the words to Von Tilzer in Chicago in 1899. He immediately saw their possibilities, but insisted that the text make it entirely clear that the heroine was married to the old man.   The necessary revisions were made, and with the manuscript in his pocket and virtuous thoughts in his heart, Mr. Von Tilzer went on a party which ended in a roadhouse of no very savoury reputation.

While others disported themselves in ribald fashion, the young composer sat down at the piano, and in no time at all he had turned out the tune which was to send the "Bird" flying all over America. He sang it over several times, when he suddenly noticed that some of the girls were crying.   "If these ladies weep real tears over my song," he said to himself, "I believe I have composed a hit."   And so, in truth, it proved.

The complete song may be found in Harry Von Tilzer's "Collection of Old Time Favourite Hits," and a suggestion of the music will be sufficient here.   The verses tell the heartrending story as follows:

A BIRD IN A GILDED CAGE

The ball-room was filled with fashion's throng,[1]
   It shone with a thousand lights,
And there was a woman who passed along,
   The fairest of all the sights.[2]

---

[1] Evidently a party was going on.   The setting was just right for establishing the creative mood.
[2] This merely means that the other women were sights, not the heroine.

A girl to her lover then softly sighed
"There's riches at her command":
"But she married for wealth, not for love," he cried,[3]
"Though she lives in a mansion grand."

Then comes the chorus in the traditional waltz-time:

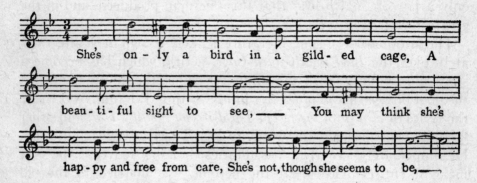

She's on-ly a bird in a gild-ed cage, A
beau-ti-ful sight to see, ___ You may think she's
hap-py and free from care, She's not, though she seems to be, ___

'Tis sad when you think of her wasted life,
For youth cannot mate with age,
And her beauty was sold for an old man's gold,[4]
She's a bird in a gilded cage.

The second verse completes the picture:

I stood in a church-yard just at eve,[5]
When sunset adorned the West,
And looked at the people who'd come to grieve
For loved ones now laid at rest.
A tall marble monument marked the grave
Of one who'd been fashion's queen,
And I thought, "She is happier here at rest,
Than to have people say when seen":[6]   [*Chorus*]

(Copyright, 1900, by Shapiro, Bernstein & Von Tilzer; Jerome H. Remick & Co., New York and Detroit.   Used by permission of the composer.)

Two years later, when the *Gilded Cage* had turned into solid gold, Arthur Lamb brought Mr. Von Tilzer another lyric of the same

---

[3]It was this line that was made specifically proper, at the composer's request.

[4]Only two of the three rhymes are intentional. There are good bird's-eye swipes on "sold," "gold," and "gild."

[5]The story seems to be taken up by the poet himself, who again finds himself conveniently in just the right spot at the right time.

[6]People always feel that they have to say something, when they are unexpectedly seen.

type, *The Mansion of Aching Hearts*, and again a successful song
resulted. This time, however, the proprieties were less carefully
guarded, and many is the letter the composer has received, asking
what kind of a mansion this was, anyhow. The chorus is non-
committal:

> She lives in a mansion of aching hearts,
>   She's one of a restless throng,
> The diamonds that glitter around her throat,
>   They speak both of sorrow and song;
> The smile on her face is only a mask,
>   And many the tear that starts,
> For sadder it seems, when of mother she dreams,
>   In the mansion of aching hearts.

The lady of this pathetic story is described in the verses as "the
beautiful belle of the ball," and just before the second chorus a man
is looking at her picture (not turned to the wall) and reading her
letter:

> "Oh, try to forget that we ever have met,"
> Then he thinks with a heart full of pain: [*Chorus*]

Whatever the dark secret may be, it is certainly sad. The coon
songs of Harry Von Tilzer offer a more cheerful prospect.

I'd Leave Ma Happy Home for You was the first "novelty coon
song," and the parent of a long line that still persists. The story
of its creation is vouched for by the composer himself.

It seems there was a show called "The Prodigal Father" playing
in Hartford, Connecticut, and Mr. Von Tilzer was the pianist.
This was in 1897. After the first performance, a young girl waited
for Harry at the stage door and confessed to him an earnest desire
to go on the stage. He did not take her seriously, but jokingly
suggested that, when the engagement ended, she might pack her
trunk and come along.

The young Thespian thought no more of the matter, but on
Saturday night, to his great surprise, there was the girl, with a
check for her trunk, all ready to go. Explanations followed, and
a vivid description of the difficulties of stage life. "Where do you

live, little girl?" he asked, kindly. She took him around and showed him a beautiful mansion, obviously a home of wealth and refinement. This, of course, inspired a telling sermon on the folly of giving up such comforts for the danger and drudgery of the road. Then the truth came out.

"I'd leave my happy home for you," she cried, on the verge of tears.

The line had a stronger appeal than the girl. He left her with the fateful words ringing in his heart and immediately wrote his first great black-face success, leaving it to Will A. Heelan to polish up the details of the lyric.

While the Negro dialect is rather spasmodic in this song, it contains unmistakable evidences of the unique Von Tilzer gift of fitting a text with a natural ragtime. (Several years earlier this same composer had made the first use on record of the term "ragtime" in a song title.) Blanche Ring introduced it at Tony Pastor's Theatre, and made her own reputation as well as that of the song.

Here are the words, with a suggestion of the syncopated chorus:

I'D LEAVE MA HAPPY HOME FOR YOU

A gal I knew, a nice gal too,
   Till someone told her she knew how to act,
Then that baby blew every solitary sou,[1]
   Chasin' roun' to cheap theatres, that's a fact.
At last she got acquainted with an actor who was painted
   Like a darky in de show,[2]
And she followed him aroun' till the night they quit de town,
   Then she said: "Please take me with you when you go. For—

I'd leave ma hap-py home for you — oo, oo, oo, oo, ———
You're de nic-est man I ev-er knew — oo, oo, oo, oo, etc.

---

[1] This seems to place the scene in New Orleans.

[2] The poet is beginning to remember his assumed complexion and to pronounce his th's accordingly

If you take me and just break me in de business too, oo,
I'd leave ma happy home for you, oo, oo, oo, oo.[3]"

The second verse is not entirely gallant:

He said he'd shake de show and take
    That lady with a comp'ny of his own,
But he packed his grips and he took a quiet trip,
    And he left that little baby all alone.
He tried his best to skip her, but she used to buy de *Clipper*,[4]
    What de actors' news was in,
When she found out where he went, every day a note she sent,
    This is just how every letter would begin: Well— [*Chorus*]

Von Tilzer's best coon song, and probably one of the greatest
ever written, is *Alexander*. (The establishing of the name was
unquestionably helpful to Irving Berlin's later hit, *Alexander's
Ragtime Band.*)

The team of McIntyre and Heath was responsible for this inspiration, along with an actual rainstorm. The composer had
been watching their vaudeville act, and noted that McIntyre consistently referred to Heath as "Alexander," and that the name
always got a laugh. With the upward inflection of the voice, it
began to shape itself as a syncopated phrase in Harry's mind.

As he came out of the theatre, it was raining heavily, and while
he stood in the lobby, waiting for the storm to abate, the entire
chorus of *Alexander*, believe it or not, formed itself in his musical
imagination. Andrew B. Sterling later worked out the lyric,
and the song became the minstrel sensation of its day, with special
popularity throughout the South.

Here are the complete words and melody, by special permission
of the composer:

---

[3]The "oo, oo, oo" effects undoubtedly had much to do with the popularity of this song. (There
is a story that in England someone sang it "double o, double o.") Von Tilzer had already written
a "Goo-goo Eyes" song, and this thought, like the crooning vowels of the chorus above, found im-
mortality in its imitators.

[4]The famous theatrical sheet, known to everyone in the profession.

Look here, Al - ex - an - der, I was on - ly fool - ing,

When I said an - oth - er coon my heart was rul - ing,

All the day __ I think of no one else __ but you, ____

Hon - est, Al - ex - an - der, won't you please be - lieve __ me?

It would break my heart in two if you should leave __ me,

Won't you take __ me back, babe, and I'll al - ways be true; __

Nev - er let an - oth - er man make eyes at me, ____

I'll be just as sweet as an - y gal can be __

You can be the "Boss," I'll let you have your way, __

Al - ex - an - der won't you let me stay? __

Can't you see the rain and hail am fast - ly fall - ing Al - ex - an - der? ____

____ Don't you hear your la - dy love a - soft - ly call - ing, Al - ex -

an - der?_____ Take me to your heart a-gain and call me hon - ey;

All I want is lov - in', I don't want your mon - ey, Al - ex -

an-der tell me, don't you love your ba - by no more?_____

Look here, Alexander, say that you remember,
You ain't done a stroke of work since last December.
Who went out a-washin', worked all day for you?
Listen, Alexander, you were keepin' cases,
While I took in scrubbin', you just played the races,
Say if that ain't love, babe, no gal ever loved true;
I don't want to talk about the things I've done,
I just want to say that you're ma only one,
I'll put up a washin' sign outside the door,
Alexander take me back once more.   [Chorus]

In a sense, *Alexander* was the answer to another Von Tilzer coon song, *Good-bye, Eliza Jane*, written a year earlier, also with a Sterling text.   In this case, it is the coloured gentleman who is dismissing his lady-love in no uncertain terms, and it is only because of the later song that one dares hope the quarrel may eventually have been made up.

The parallel of *Dat's Where My Money Goes* will occur to the reminiscent reader who hums the start of the chorus:

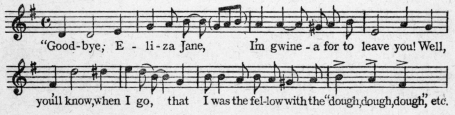

"Good-bye; E - li - za Jane,   I'm gwine - a for to leave you! Well,

you'll know, when I go,   that I was the fel-low with the "dough, dough, dough," etc.

Still another classic of the "coon-song" school is *What You Goin' to Do when the Rent Comes 'Round?* also known by the compound name of its protagonist, Rufus Rastus Johnson Brown. Here again a bit of real life provided the necessary suggestion.

Harry Von Tilzer was standing on the platform of the railway station at Miami, listening to the conversation of two Negroes. The woman was berating the man, and after using every possible adjective to describe his low-down shiftlessness, she worked up to a climax with the question, "What you goin' to do when de rent comes 'round?" The rest was easy.

As usual, bad weather entered into the final version of the story, as lyricized by the ever-ready Sterling, and it is worth noting that such later successes as *Bill Bailey* and *Ain't Dat a Shame?* are all imitations of these originals.

The words of the chorus will suggest the tune, which is to be found in the regular Von Tilzer collection:

> Rufus Rastus Johnson Brown,
> What you goin' to do when the rent comes 'round?
> What you goin' to say? How you goin' to pay?
> You'll never have a bit of sense till Judgment Day;
> You know, I know, rent means dough,
> Landlord's goin' to put us out in the snow,
> Rufus Rastus Johnson Brown,
> What you goin' to do when the rent comes round?

Aside from such ticklings of the coloured comic Muse, Harry Von Tilzer caught something of the real Southern spirit in his fine close-harmony chorus, *Picture To-night a Field of Snowy White*, whose real title is *Down Where the Cotton Blossoms Grow*.

In the realm of the "gang song," however, this composer made his ten-strike. Breathes there a man with soul so dead, whose voice has never yet been led to waken from its dull repose, and sing *Down Where the Wurzburger Flows?*

Even the Volstead Act did not stop the spread of this rousing chorus, and to-day Harry Von Tilzer is plugging its legitimate descendant, *Under a Wurzburger Tree*. Here is the true history of the original booster of bottled goods:

In the course of rehearsing George Lederer's "Wild Rose" production (in which, incidentally, Evelyn Nesbit had her first speaking part), it was found that a drinking-song was required. Suiting the action to the word, Vincent P. Bryan and Harry Von Tilzer put their heads and steins together, but nothing came of it at the moment.

That evening, however, as they were going in to dinner at a restaurant, Von Tilzer remembered a current song, *Down on the Brandywine*, in which a small Pennsylvania stream is celebrated with a suggestion of something stronger than water. A Wurzburger label may have aided in speeding up production. At any rate, the composer suddenly found himself repeating, "Down on the Brandywine, down on the Wurzburger, down where the Wurzburger flows."

"No dinner bells for me," he almost shouted, as he dragged his lyric-writer to a piano. In less than the time of a table d'hôte, it was finished.

Then came a disappointment. Harry B. Smith, the librettist of the "Wild Rose" show, decided that if it was drinking-songs that were wanted, he could write them himself, and for a time the liquid lyric languished.

With characteristic faith in his work, however, Von Tilzer took the song to Nora Bayes, then just breaking into vaudeville. She liked it, and they planted its introduction at Percy Williams's Orpheum Theatre in Brooklyn. Von Tilzer himself sat in a stage box, and after Miss Bayes had sung the first chorus, he took the encore. There were fourteen recalls at the first performance, and the management hired Harry to sit in the box the rest of the week. Meanwhile, he and Nora plugged the song in the restaurants all over town, singing it whenever they could get a crowd together, and then making the crowd sing it, too.

For a long time Nora Bayes was known as "the Wurzburger Girl," and eventually she carried the song to London, where the treasured *Times* inquired why she did not sing about the Thames instead of some "western American stream."

Drink-songs galore followed the current of the Wurzburger, but none approached its success, although Von Tilzer himself did nicely with his *Under the Anhauser Busch,* and there was a pleasantly sparkling champagne song that contained the couplet,

The platform I stand on
Is Moët and Chandon.

It is a pleasure to give the complete text and melody of *Down Where the Wurzburger Flows* herewith:

Now po-ets may sing of the dear Fa-ther-land, And the soft flow-ing dream-y old Rhine, — Be-side the Blue Dan-ube in fan-cy they stand, And they rave of its beau-ties di-vine. — But there is a spot where the sun nev-er shines, Where mirth and good fel-low-ship reign, — For dear old Bo-hem-ia my lone-ly heart pines, And I long to be there once a-gain. — Take me down, down, down where the Wurz-burg-er flows, flows, flows, — It goes down, down, down, but no-bod-y knows where it goes. — Just or-der two seid-els of la-ger, or three, If I

The second line of the chorus is generally sung, "It will drown, drown, drown all your sorrows and cares and woes," and rightly.

A seidel is a fairly large measure, originally designed for beer. Lager, literally "camp" (German), is a beer that could be drunk there, or anywhere else for that matter.

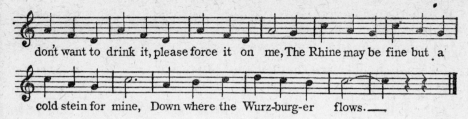

don't want to drink it, please force it on me, The Rhine may be fine but a cold stein for mine, Down where the Wurz-burg-er flows.___

The Rhine by moonlight's a beautiful sight,
When the wind whispers low thro' the vines,
But give me some good old Rathskeller at night,
Where the brilliant electric light shines.
The poets may think it's delightful to hear
The nightingale piping his lay,
Give me a piano, a cold stein of beer
And a fellow who knows how to play[1]   [*Chorus*]

(Copyright, 1902, by Harry Von Tilzer Music Pub. Co.   Used by permission.)

Another great gang song, with splendid possibilities for close harmony, is *Wait Till the Sun Shines, Nellie*, Von Tilzer's own pet, and one of his biggest money-makers. A newspaper story, read by the composer in the lobby of the old Breslin Hotel, provided the impetus for this sentimental weather report.

It told of an East Side family, fallen upon misfortune, but luckily discovered by an altruistic journalist, who predicted that after the storm had passed, the sun would shine, which has actually happened many times, as any close observer can testify. The name "Nellie" was one of those happy choices that come to all composers now and then, and the result was an unforgettable title.

Banks Winter, composer of *White Wings* (which refers to sails, not street-cleaners), picked *Wait Till the Sun Shines, Nellie*, as a hit, and it was his daughter Winona who introduced it in vaudeville. After the San Francisco earthquake, this song provided a melodic strain of optimism, with "Frisco" substituted for "Nellie."

Many years later, when things were not breaking so well for Harry Von Tilzer, he received a letter from Elizabeth Murray containing the line "Just around the corner the sun will shine for you." It gave him the necessary follow-up to the Nellie idea,

---

[1]The modern parallel to Omar's book of verses, jug of wine, loaf of bread, etc.

and *Just Around the Corner* is perhaps the biggest Von Tilzer success of the past few years.

The chorus of *Wait Till the Sun Shines, Nellie,* is so familiar that no crowd should need more than a fair start:

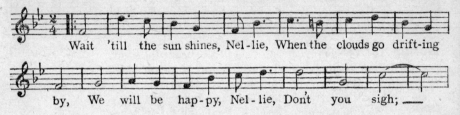

Wait   'till   the sun shines, Nel-lie, When the   clouds go   drift-ing   by,   We   will   be   hap-py, Nel-lie, Don't   you   sigh; ___

Down lovers' lane we'll wander, sweetheart, you and I;
Wait till the sun shines, Nellie, bye and bye.

The verses, however, are not so well known, and as they tell a Sweet Story, they are worth quoting:

On a Sunday Morn sat a maid forlorn,
    With her sweetheart by her side;
Through the window-pane she looked at the rain,
    "We must stay home, Joe," she cried.
"There's a picnic, too, at the Old Point View,
    It's a shame it rained to-day."
Then the boy drew near, kissed away each tear,
    And she heard him softly say: [*Chorus*]

"How I long," she sighed, "for a trolley ride,
    Just to show my brand new gown";
Then she gazed on high with a gladsome cry,
    For the sun came shining down.
And she looked so sweet on the big front seat,
    As the car sped on its way,
And she whispered low, "Say, you're all right, Joe,
    You just won my heart to-day." [*Chorus*]

(*Copyright, 1902, by Harry Von Tilzer Music Pub. Co.   Used by permission.*)

ON A SUNDAY AFTERNOON

Here is still another of the community songs that made Von Tilzer's reputation, and, according to the composer, the one that reached hit proportions faster than any other in his list. Harry claims that he dreamed this song, so why not take him at his word?

The atmosphere that created *On a Sunday Afternoon* was very much that of the *Feldeinsamkeit* of Brahms, although, of course, the results were quite different. At any rate, it was the first of a long line to celebrate the joys of the vacation season, including *The Good Old Summertime* and many others.

Von Tilzer was sitting on a bench, enjoying the balmy quiet of a summer Sunday, and gradually dozing off under the spell. During this semiconscious state, a lilting waltz chorus gradually forced itself upon his inner ear. When he reached the line, "They work hard on Monday, but one day that's fun day," he awoke suddenly to the realization that another hit had been conceived.

Hurrying home, he got the whole thing down on paper, with the help of the indefatigable Sterling, and within ten days all the department stores of New York were selling the song, which went over the million mark in an incredibly short time.

On the Old Fall River Line was a natural follow-up more than ten years later, and it also did well by its composer. The geography and sociology of the Sunday afternoon song are familiar to every New Yorker, even to-day. You should hear the Ritz Quartet do it as part of their medley, with patter decorations and a "hot dog" at the finish!

It is presented herewith, sans apologies or explanations, as a model of its kind:

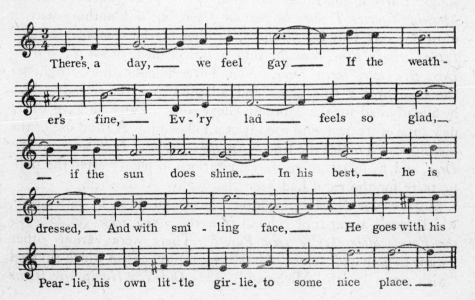

There's a day,— we feel gay— If the weather's fine,— Ev-'ry lad— feels so glad,—
— if the sun does shine.— In his best,— he is
dressed,— And with smi-ling face,— He goes with his
Pear-lie, his own lit-tle gir-lie, to some nice place.—

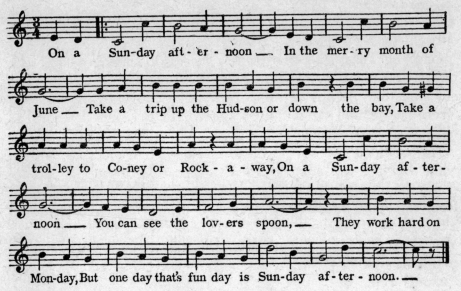

On a Sun-day aft-er-noon — In the mer-ry month of June — Take a trip up the Hud-son or down the bay, Take a trol-ley to Co-ney or Rock-a-way, On a Sun-day af-ter-noon — You can see the lov-ers spoon, — They work hard on Mon-day, But one day that's fun day is Sun-day af-ter-noon. —

Coming home, starry dome with a soft moonshine,
Lovers kiss, oh what bliss, oh what joy divine.
"Good-night, Joe." "Good-night, Flo, don't forget now, dear,
Next Sunday at two, I'll be waiting for you on the Old Iron Pier." *[Chorus]*

The versatile Von Tilzer also left his mark on the rural type of song. Early in his career he composed a piece called *Where the Morning Glories Twine Around the Door*, but did nothing with it until one day Howard Graham, brother of the composer of *Two Little Girls in Blue*, brought him a lyric called, *When the Harvest Days Are Over, Jessie Dear*. Von Tilzer bought this outright for the sake of the title alone and adapted to it the melody which he already had for the Morning Glory song. Later he gave this a new tune of its own, and used it as a follow-up. A third use of the idea appeared under the title *When the Goldenrod Is Waving, Annie, Dear*, and, as usual, there were imitations in plenty after the public taste for the rural had been thoroughly established.

Down on the Farm was another successful pæan of agriculture, which found a war-time echo in *How you gonna keep 'em down on the Farm, after they've seen Paree?* There were various other "want to go back" songs, of hazy geography, one of which rhymed "wish again" with "Michigan." (*My Old New Hampshire Home* was really the first great hit of this type, but Von Tilzer sold this outright for a pittance.)

One Von Tilzer song that made a success in spite of a bad break on the first planting was *Please Go 'Way and Let Me Sleep.* The old minstrel, Arthur Deming, introduced this at the Chicago Opera House, and the composer worked out a trick that seemed to have great possibilities.

He bought a seat in the theatre, and pretended to go to sleep while Deming was singing the first chorus. As soon as the applause had stopped, a loud snore drifted upon the air. Deming, from the stage, began an exaggerated protest against working in a theatre where they allowed the patrons to go to sleep, and finally Von Tilzer, in a maudlin voice, started the second chorus.

But he was too good an actor, and the ushers, ignorant of the "plant," promptly threw him out of the theatre. He went back the next day and tried the same trick, with precisely the same result. In fact, he was put out of the Chicago Opera House every day for a week, at great expense.

By that time, however, the song had become established, the newspapers had played up the story satisfactorily, and a tradition began which still rules, that every suggestion of sleep, in the movies or vaudeville, must be accompanied by this one tune. Here are the words, with a reminder of its gently somnolescent chorus:

> I am twice as happy as a millionaire,
>   Every day I have such lovely dreams,
> When I'm sleepin' money never gives me a care,
>   Trouble never troubles me, it seems.
> I don't mind no summer heat or wintry storm,
>   When I turn in bed, I feel the Spring,[1]
> 'Larm clocks act on me just like a dose of chloroform,
>   When folks tries to wake me up I sings:

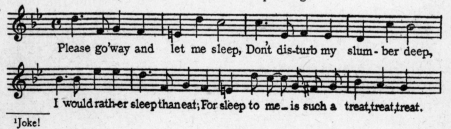

Please go'way and let me sleep, Don't dis-turb my slum-ber deep,
I would rath-er sleep than eat; For sleep to me — is such a treat, treat, treat.

[1] Joke!

I never had a dream so nice, Thought I was in Paradise,
Wakin' up makes me feel cheap, So please let me sleep.

Ten o'clock this mornin' I was poundin' my ear,
    Dreamin' I'm the warmest coon in town,
Landlord hollered "Wake up, quick, an' get out of here,
    Hurry up, the place is burning down."
I got sore at bein' woke an' started to shout,
    "Stop that noise out there, for goodness' sake.
I can't watch no fire now, so you can put it out,
    Burn your blamed old house when I'm awake." [*Chorus*]

That is about enough of Von Tilzer for this book.   It should be
added, however, that his *Cubanola Glide* was the first dance song
of the type that afterward developed the Grizzly Bear, Turkey Trot,
Bunny Hug, etc.   Harriet Raymond introduced it in "The Girl
from Rector's," and it was an important milestone in the career
of Sophie Tucker.   The idea actually came from Cuba, and a line
of the chorus is enough to emphasize its individuality of rhythm:

THE CUBANOLA GLIDE

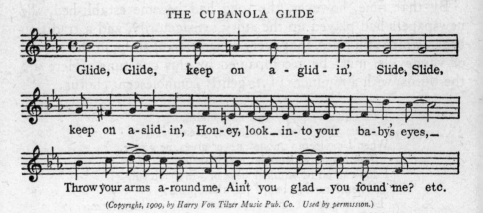

Glide, Glide, keep on a-glid-in', Slide, Slide,
keep on a-slid-in', Hon-ey, look in-to your ba-by's eyes,
Throw your arms a-round me, Ain't you glad you found me? etc.

Vincent Bryan's words are not particularly elevating, but compared with some modern lyrics they are Sunday-school home-work.
The original *All Alone* (Von Tilzer's) was the first song to use an
actual telephone on the stage.   *Take Me Back to New York Town*
was first written for London and afterward Americanized.   Lina
Cavalieri selected *Last Night Was the End of the World* for her first
American tour.   *Under the Yum Yum Tree* was a concession to the

jungle cycle which included Cole and Johnson's *Under the Bamboo Tree*, *My Little Chimpanzee*, and several others.

The cynical attitude toward marriage which struck America's song-writers about 1908 was reflected in Von Tilzer's *Don't Take Me Home* and *I Love My Wife, but oh You Kid*, which belong in the same group with *No Wedding Bells for Me*, *There Was I a-waitin' at the Church*, *Afraid to Go Home in the Dark*, *Poor John*, and *Don't Get Married any More, Ma*.

On the other hand, *I Want a Girl Just Like the Girl That Married dear old Dad* is still a home favourite, with great possibilities for sentimental harmonizing. All in all, considerable song-writer, Mr. Von Tilzer!

THE TATTOOED LADY

One of the immediate results of the taste for geographical songs was a series of parodies, of which the best loved (and most printable) is *The Tattooed Lady*, to the tune of *My Home in Tennessee*. This is decidedly English, of course, but it seems to have appealed equally to the American sense of humour.

The appended version emerges from the collaboration of three modern students of literature, Miss Katharine Lane, Miss Lucie Taussig, and Miss Maggie Toohey, who, so far as the editor knows, could beat any tattoo that ever was invented.

I paid a bob to see The tattooed Scotch lady,[1]
Tattooed from head to knee, She was a sight to see.
For over her jaw Was a British man-o'-war,[2]
While on her back Was the Union Jack, And could one ask for more?
All up and down her spine Was the King's horse guard in line,
And all about her hips Was a line of battleships,
And over one kidney Was a bird's-eye view of Sydney,
But what I liked best, Across her chest Was my home in Tennessee.

She Was Bred in Old Kentucky is another song remembered today by its parodies rather than by the original. Harry Braisted and Stanley Carter were responsible for its authorship, and its

---

[1]Or "lassie."

[2]There are variants which insist that "'round about her jaw was a map of Canada," and mention also a porpoise, a "couple of spouting whales," and the Eddystone Light, besides naming a few public characters, flowers, etc.

first interpreter was Lottie Gilson. It was revived by the Klein Brothers in the "Gaieties of 1919."

The most reputable of the satiric versions began:

> She was bread in Old Kentucky, she was cake in New Orleans,
> She was pie in Louisiana, and in Boston she was beans.

For the rougher element there was ecstasy in the slapstick humour of *The Blow Almost Killed Father*.

Many have not yet forgotten the exquisite stanza about the mule (or was it a horse?):

> Father had an old grey mule, With a cold down in his thorax,
> Put a gas pipe down his throat, Filled with powdered borax.
> Said Pa, "Now you hold on this end, While I blow down the other."
> Pa he blowed, the mule he coughed, And the blow almost killed father.

Song-writing paid its tribute to the vogue of the Gibson pictures, in the late 'Nineties, with *Why Do They Call Me a Gibson Girl?* and an early "bathing beauty" chorus, *Mr. Gibson, Mr. Gibson, Can't We Go in to Swim?* Both were lilting waltz tunes.

The transfiguration of "like" from a preposition to a conjunction has been prominent in all American song lyrics, and several choruses have concentrated doggedly upon popularizing this comparatively harmless crime against the English language. One of Miss Imogen Comer's hits at Koster & Bial's in the 'Nineties submitted the following:

> I love you like a copper loves to sleep,
>   And like a little newsboy loves a pie—
> I love you like a baby loves to creep—
>   Well, if I don't love you, Mame, I hope to die!
> I love you like the kids love street pianos,
>   I love you like a gambler loves a game,
> Just like the Reuben loves the Tenderloin—I love you!
> *Spoken*: Well, say kid—That's how I love you, Mame!

Joe McCarthy, however, later improved on this when he wrote in one of those Feist songs with which complete propriety is guaranteed

> Like the roses need their fragrance, Like a sweetheart needs a kiss,
> Like a summer needs the sunshine, Like a laddie needs a miss;
> Like a broken heart needs gladness, Like the flowers need the dew,
> Like a baby needs its mother, That's how I need you.

THE CHARLIE CASE SONGS

The first man to ridicule effectively the absurdities of the Nineteenth Century ballad style was Charlie Case, a black-face comedian who made a unique name for himself as a creator and singer of parodies.[1] Two of his most popular burlesques are given below.

The interpreter of a Case song should sing in a very matter-of-fact voice, with little or no expression, letting the words speak for themselves. F. Gregory Hartswick, of the New York *World*, one of the original cross-word puzzle editors, is an expert also in the Charlie Case idiom, and does equally well with ukulele or piano accompaniment. These are his versions of two intensely interesting lyric stories. (Just follow the general outline of the melody, letting the important accents fall where they are marked on the words.):

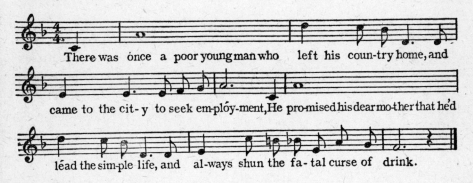

There was once a poor young man who left his coun-try home, and came to the cit-y to seek em-plóy-ment, He pro-mised his dear mo-ther that he'd léad the sim-ple life, and al-ways shun the fa- tal curse of drink.

He cáme to the city and accepted emplóyment in a quarry,
    And while thére he made the acquaintance of some college mén;
He líttle guessed that they were demons, for they wóre the best of clothes,
    But clóthes do not álways make the gentleman.

One níght he went out with his néw-found friends to dine,
    And they tríed to persuade him to take a drínk;
They témpted him and tempted him, but he refúsed and he refused,
    Till fínallý he took a glass of beer.

---

[1]Case's untimely death was supposedly due to the accidental explosion of a gun that he was cleaning, but it is generally recognized in the theatrical profession that he shot himself. Mixed blood was the chief reason.

When he seén what he had done he dashed the líquor to the floor
　And stággered through the door with delirium trémens;
While ín the grip of liquor he met a Salvátion Army lassie,
　And crúelly he broke her tambourine.

All she sáid was "Heaven bless you!" and placed a márk upon his brow
　With a kíck that she had learned before she was sáved;
So kind fríends, take my advice and shun the fátal curse of drink,
　And dón't go aróund breaking people's tambourines.

This works to the same tune:

There was ónce a poor young girl who léft her country home,
　And cáme to the city to seek emplóyment;
She hád to leave her home because the wólf was at the door
　And her fáther had fállen down and hurt his knee.

Just befóre she went away her sweétheart, whose name was Jack,
　Said to hér "I fear you will not be true."
And só she had to promise him before she gót on the train
　That évery níght at eight o'clock she would burst into tears.

She cáme to the city, and was ríding on a street car
　When a mán got up and offered her his séat;
She refúsed the offer with scorn, for she sáw that he wore a ring,
　And she dídn't knów but that he might be a married man.

Then úp came the conductor and said "I knéw you would be true!"
　And tóre off his false whiskers, and it was Jáck!
And that dáy she got a telegram saying that her fáther's knee was better
　And an aúnt had diéd and left her $58,000.00.

DON'T SWAT YOUR MOTHER

Brian Hooker, librettist of the American prize opera, "Mona," and a poet of parts, has an affectionate understanding of the home life of the sentimental ballad, and his collection, which has contributed much to this volume, is probably unique in its way.

In collaboration with Porter Steele, Mr. Hooker has issued a pamphlet of parodies, "Four Heart-Songs of Hearth and Home,"[1] of

<hr>

[1] Published by M. Steinert, Boston, Mass.

which the best known is called *Don't Swat Your Mother, 'Cause It's Mean*. This burlesque of the "Mother" songs of the past seems almost brutal until we remember that the originals were just about as bad, in fact worse, because they were taken seriously.

Following are the words and music of Messrs. Hooker and Steele's crashing caricature:

Home-ward to their moth-er, — two work-ing men did come, —
Wea-ry with their hon-est toil and light-ed up with rum. —
Sup-per was not rea-dy. — One aim'd a brut-al blow, When the
blue-eyed ba-by stopp'd them, say-ing "Broth-ers, don't do so. —
Don't swat yer moth-er, boys, just 'cause she's old! Don't mop the
floor with her face. — Think how her love is a treas-ure of gold,
Shin-ing thro' shame and dis-grace. — Don't put the rock-ing-chair
next to her eye, Don't bounce the lamp off her bean! — An-gels are
watch-ing you up in the sky, Don't swat yer moth-er, it's mean!" —

Anger was arrested,—
The strong men bowed in tears;—
They were kinder to their parent
Through her few remaining years.—

Now her place is vacant—
Of her they sit and dream,
While the memories awakened
In their hearts to say will seem: [*Chorus*]

(*Copyright, 1919, by Brian Hooker and Porter Steele.   Used by permission.*)

EVERYBODY WORKS BUT FATHER

Another song that appeared early in the Twentieth Century and did its share in upsetting the filial reverence of the newer generation was *Everybody Works but Father*. The words were by Charles W. McClintock, but the most popular tune to which they were sung was of old English origin.[1]

Mr. McClintock implied that "Father" was a thoroughly lazy person. (This of course was long before *Life with Father* had become a permanent part of the American scene, through the combined ministrations of Clarence Day, Russel Crouse and Howard Lindsay.)   Mother and Sister Ann really supported the family by taking in washing, but the "old man" merely sat at home all day, with his feet against the fire-place, "smoking his pipe of clay." It was customary to end the chorus with a parenthetical insult, in which Father was called a "loafer," preceded by the traditional blanks to indicate profanity.

DON'T TELL ME WHAT YOU DREAMED LAST NIGHT
(*For I've Been Reading Freud*)

This is the contribution of Franklin P. Adams to the newer literature of burlesque ballads. The psychology, of course, is ultra-modern, as might be expected from the editor of "The Conning Tower."   Brian Hooker composed the music, of which the quotation of the chorus should suffice here:

A débutante was sitting in the corner of her flat,
A brave young man upon her he was calling;
They talked about the weather and the war, and things like that,
As couples will, for conversation stalling.

---

[1]An American melody was later written by Samuel Lehman and published by the Edward B. Marks Music Co.

The talk it all went well until at last the young man said:
"Last night I dreamed that you had gone away."
The débutante put up her hand, and stopped that young man dead,
And softly in his ear these words did say:

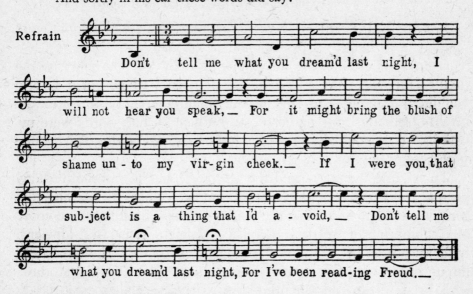

Refrain

Don't tell me what you dream'd last night, I will not hear you speak,— For it might bring the blush of shame un-to my vir-gin cheek.— If I were you, that sub-ject is a thing that I'd a-void,— Don't tell me what you dream'd last night, For I've been read-ing Freud.—

A loving husband sat one morn at breakfast with his wife,
And said to her, "Please, Minnie, pass the crea-um.
Last night I dreamed that Fritzi Scheff pursued me with a knife,
And though I tried, I could not even screa-um."
The little wife put up her hand, and said, "Oh, pray, desist.
Disclosures such as these will break my heart.
That dream, I fear, is plain to any psychoanalyst."
And then she softly wept, and said in part: [*Chorus pp second time*]

WE MODERNS

For the past twenty-five years, popular music has become more and more a matter of professional performance and less and less concentrated around the home piano. The phonograph was the first factor to cut into the wide distribution of sheet music and to eliminate the necessity of parlour amateurs. For a time, the profits from the "mechanicals" to both publishers and composers were so enormous that nobody worried much about the decline in home singing.

Then came the radio, and the returns from the records subsided into a comparatively thin line of smoke. With the parallel development of the dance craze, a popular song no longer had to be a combination of words and music. A mere tune was sufficient, and this tune, in a majority of cases, was borrowed, consciously or unconsciously, from some other music of the past.

The last of the old school of song-writing specialized in the ragtime style (originating in the "coon songs" of the 'Nineties) "gang songs," like *The Good Old Summertime*, and those geographical advertisements of various towns, states, and sections of the country in which it was argued that any one would be happier than he was where Fate had placed him.

The dance mania was first prophesied in a succession of syncopated fantasies glorifying some particular step (with the assurance that *Everybody's Doing It*) and giving it a highly descriptive and perhaps suggestive name, frankly taken from the animal life which it was disposed to imitate. (Actual "animal songs" have always had a fascination for human beings.)

With the jazz movement rushing on to a climax of hysteria, the inevitable reaction has already set in, and to-day there is a marked revival of the simple, old-fashioned tunes, which radio listeners in particular seem to prefer to the exaggerated complexities and jazzy distortions of the newer dance-music.

Irving Berlin, the undisputed champion among modern hit-writers, has contributed his full share to the ragtime spirit, but his greatest successes, nevertheless, have been of the ballad type. Such composers as Victor Herbert, Jerome Kern, Friml, and Romberg have kept alive the appreciation of honest melody, and the newest genius in the popular field, George Gershwin, may actually prove to be the long missing link between the taste of the masses and the approval of the intelligentsia.

All the world still loves a tune, as it always has and always will.

The songs that have appeared since 1900 are mostly available in collections or sheet music, and do not require much discussion. Leo Feist, Inc., have issued a collection consisting largely of medleys, in which may be found the choruses of such great hits as *The Good Old Summertime, K-k-k-Katy, Over There, Rose of No Man's Land, Peg o' My Heart, When You Wore a Tulip, You're Here and I'm Here*, etc., in addition to the cream of the 'Nineties.

J. Bodewalt Lampe, an expert arranger of modern jazz, has edited a collection for the house of Remick, which includes *Bedelia, By the Light of the Silvery Moon, Chinatown, Creole Belle, Dreaming, In the Shade of the Old Apple Tree, Pony Boy, Navajo, Put on Your Old Grey Bonnet, What's the Matter with Father?*, and *Mr. Dooley*.

Nicholas De Vore, in a book of "Fifty Famous Favourites," has added to the readily available material the typical Cohan songs, such as *Give My Regards to Broadway, The Yankee Doodle Boy, You're a Grand old Flag, Mary Is a Grand old Name*, and *So Long, Mary*, as well as *Waiting for the Robert E. Lee* and a lot of old-timers. There have been dance songs, animal songs, geographical songs, sentimental songs, nonsense songs, production songs (adapted to spectacular stage effects in musical comedy and the later revues) and plenty of others, and standards have suffered by overproduction. One hit, containing an original idea, or some real musical value, has inevitably bred a whole tribe of imitators, and in some cases the imitations did better than the originals.

Song-writers and publishers are just as far as ever from being able to prognosticate exactly what the public will like.

It was in 1903 that a new and fascinating Irish fantasy bowled over the American public—*Bedelia*, by Billy Jerome and Jean Schwartz, with that gorgeous rhyme to start its chorus: "Bedelia, I want to steal ye," and with a musical appeal very similar to that of *Valencia* to-day. A year earlier the world had begun to sing *Mr. Dooley* with affectionate recognition of the character created by Finley Peter Dunne and still commenting actively on public affairs.

According to the song, Mr. Dooley was responsible for most of the events of history ascribed to others, or at least coöperated in them. He "called down" Napoleon's army, saved the day at San Juan Hill, invented Wireless Telegraphy ("To Edison he taught a thing or two, And young Marconi eats macaroni, Along with Mr. Dooley, ooley-oo"), cut down Washington's cherry tree, settled all the strikes, advised the Kaiser and beat Prince Henry drinking beer, greeted Columbus on his arrival, succeeded Ward McAllister as leader of the Four Hundred, wrote the jokes for Chauncey M. Depew ("It seems that Chauncey took quite a fauncy To the jokes of Mr. Dooley, ooley-oo"), and finally made the reputation of Doctor Munyon, who, for the sake of the rhyme, "cured a bunion" on the immortal Irish foot.

Another song with endless verses of the "topical" variety was that epic of New York politics, *Tammany*, written in 1905 by Vincent Bryan and Gus Edwards, and introduced by Jefferson de Angelis in "Fantana." It was "respectfully dedicated to the Hon. Timothy D. Sullivan," and its music is an irresistible urge to the traditional Indian warcry (made, as everyone knows, by tapping the palm of the hand against the open mouth and saying "wah" in a high-pitched voice).

A few characteristic verses are sufficient. The flavour lasts:

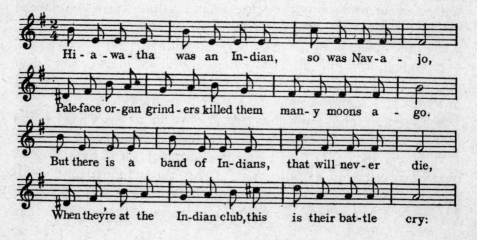

Hi - a - wa - tha was an In-dian, so was Nav-a - jo,

Pale-face or-gan grind-ers killed them man-y moons a - go.

But there is a band of In-dians, that will nev-er die,

When they're at the In-dian club, this is their bat-tle cry:

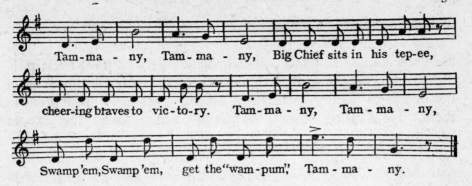

Tam-ma - ny, Tam-ma - ny, Big Chief sits in his tep-ee, cheer-ing braves to vic-to-ry. Tam-ma - ny, Tam-ma - ny, Swamp'em, Swamp'em, get the "wam-pum", Tam - ma - ny.

Chris Colombo sailed from Spain, across the deep blue sea,
Brought along the Dago vote to beat out Tammany.
Tammany found Colombo's crew were living on a boat,
Big Chief said: "They're floaters," and he would not let them vote,
Then to the tribe he wrote:

Chorus: Tammany, Tammany,
          Get those Dagoes jobs at once, they can vote in twelve more months.
          Tammany, Tammany,
          Make those floaters Tammany voters, Tammany.

Fifteen thousand Irishmen from Erin came across,
Tammany put these Irish Indians on the Police force.
I asked one cop, if he wanted three platoons or four,
He said: "Keep your old platoons, I've got a cuspidor,
What would I want with more?"

Chorus: Tammany, Tammany,
          Your policemen can't be beat, They can sleep on any street.
          Tammany, Tammany,
          Dusk is creeping, they're all sleeping, Tammany.

Of the early "gang songs" of the present century none was more
popular than *Oh, Didn't He Ramble?* (introduced by George Primrose) which is still potent enough to start a lock-step procession
around the room at almost any stag dinner. Will Handy, who
is credited with the composition of this song, was really Bob Cole,
of Cole and Johnson. There is a noticeable similarity in the lilt
of this song and that of *Mr. Dooley*.

One verse and the chorus should be a sufficient reminder:

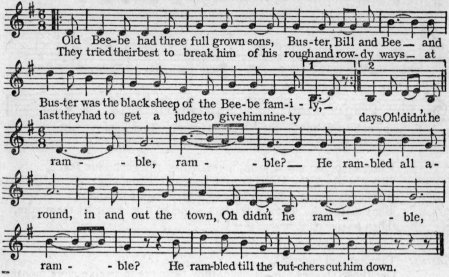

Old Bee-be had three full grown sons, Bus-ter, Bill and Bee— and
They tried their best to break him of his rough and row-dy ways— at

Bus-ter was the black sheep of the Bee-be fam-i - ly,—
last they had to get a judge to give him nine-ty   days. Oh! didn't he

ram   -   ble, ram -   - ble?— He ram-bled all a-

round, in and out the town, Oh didn't he ram   - ble,

ram -   - ble?   He ram-bled till the but-chers cut him down.

Cole and Johnson established the popularity of animal songs and the atmosphere of the forest primeval with *Under the Bamboo Tree*, and there were various jungle songs which reached a climax when Theodore Roosevelt's African hunt inspired *It's Moving Day Way Down in Jungletown*. Galloping songs (represented by the ultra-modern *Horses*, which is taken directly from Tschaikowsky's "Troika") received their chief impetus from such lively Westernisms as *Cheyenne* (punning into *Shy Anne*) *Navajo*, *Idaho*, and *Pony Boy*.

The waltz craze took its final fling with *Waltz Me Around again, Willie* and Blanche Ring's roaring specialty, *Yip I addy I ay*, although it has been proved again and again that really good waltz melodies never die. (Miss Ring also specialized in *Rings on My Fingers*, a successfully fantastic piece of Irish-Orientalism.)

Anna Held's first visit drew attention to the power and significance of the human eye. We had already had *Just Because She Made Those Goo-goo Eyes*, but after Cole and Johnson had written *The Maiden with the Dreamy Eyes* for Ziegfeld's "The Little

Duchess," it became a pet Anna Held song, and she followed it successfully with *I Just Can't Make My Eyes Behave*.

Try this on your French accent:

There are eyes of blue, There are brown eyes too, There are eyes of ev-'ry size, and eyes of ev-'ry hue; But— I sur-mise, That if you are wise, You'll be care-ful of the maid-en with the dream-y eyes.—

(*Copyright, 1901, by Jos. W. Stern & Co. Used by permission.*)

George M. Cohan long ago proved himself the master of jazz patriotism and accomplished over and over again the difficult feat of waving the flag with his tongue in his cheek and offending nobody. *The Yankee Doodle Boy* and *You're a Grand Old Flag* are models of their kind, and *Give My Regards to Broadway* is a far better song than *Over There*.

I Guess I'll Have to Telegraph My Baby and *Hello, My Baby* have set the standard for all the modern lyric discussions of the civilized means of communication, and among "name songs" a high rank must be given to *So Long, Mary*, and *Mary Is a Grand old Name* not to speak of that Irish spelling sensation, *Harrigan*.

Travel songs have maintained their popularity right up to the present day, and there was for a time a serious epidemic of threats to take a train or a boat to almost any spot that was inconvenient. *Back, Back, Back to Baltimore*, *Let Me off at Buffalo*, and *It's Forty Miles from Schenectady to Troy* were among the early specimens, and more recently we have been told of the "midnight choo-choo" that leaves for Alabam', with the hortatory *All Aboard for Dixie*, a legitimate successor to *Waiting for the Robert E. Lee*.

The popularity of the "coon song" has also never abated; in fact, the individual songs of the past have developed into complete revues of the black-and-tan variety, with a new and maudlin type of "Mammy" songs popularized by such singers as Al Jolson.

Ernest Hogan, who wrote *All Coons Look Alike to Me*, was himself a Negro, as were the great team of Cole and Johnson. Hughie Cannon, author of two enormous hits, *Ain't Dat a Shame?* and *Bill Bailey*, died a pauper, in an insane asylum. Bert Williams, originally of the team of Williams and Walker, and later an individual star, was the most practical of them all. Will his *Nobody* ever be forgotten?

There was a hint of melancholy in *Coon, Coon, Coon, I Wish My Color Would Fade* and real music in *Some of These Days* and *Shine on, Harvest Moon*. *Bill Simmons* and *Sylvester* ("much obliged to you") still live in memory, with *Jasper Johnson* ("Shame on you!")[1]

The Rural School

In addition to the steady stream of sentimentality about the advantages of living on a farm, fostered by song-writers who live in cities, there has been a significant school of rural realism in which the "rube" is given a consistent dialect and a naïve philosophy comparable with that of the more widely exploited Negro. The stock farmer song is still *Wal, I Swan* (or *Ebenezer Frye*), by Benjamin Hapgood Burt, published by the Witmarks in 1907, and in constant demand both as a solo and as a rural quartet number. The interpretation is traditionally in a high-pitched, nasal voice, with a facial expression indicating toothlessness.

Wal, I Swan! has long been a favorite with the Triangle Society of Haverford College, at whose meetings Joe Bushnell regularly sang it, with all members present joining in the chorus. Mr. Bushnell was at one time the crack banjo player of the college and later became one of its important executives.

The song has five stanzas, of which the last rhymes Joshua with Philadelphia (both giving the final vowels the sound of "ay"). Other high points are in the description of Ebenezer coming home "tighter than a drum," with Ma's comment, "'tain't possibil."

The rural school of songwriting has always had its adherents, with plenty of creators and interpreters alike to keep the customers happy. A popular old-timer had the title *Hey, Rube!* and one of the numbers in the famous Hoyt show, *A Trip to Chinatown*, was called *Reuben and Cynthia*.

In *The Bowery*, from that same hit of the musical stage, still generally familiar and prominent in the repertoire of the late Al Smith, the rural simpleton is brought to New York, to become the victim of a series of practical jokes, almost up to the modern Hollywood standard. But this rather sophisticated and often contemptuous attitude really has little connection with the sympathetic treatment of the traditional "hayseed" type.

The tendency toward sadism is perhaps best illustrated by a rare old song called *The Little Bunch of Whiskers on His Chin*, whose cruel words may be worth a complete quotation:

1.   A "Jay" came to the city once, to see the fancy sights,
      With a little bunch of whiskers on his chin;
   He'd heard about the cable cars and grand electric lights,
      With his little bunch of whiskers on his chin.
   Says he, "I'll take in everything, have all the fun I can,"
   As he got off the cars, the sharpers after him they ran,
   And quickly there in tow they had this little country man,
      With his little bunch of whiskers on his chin.

   Chorus: Reuben Glue thought he knew a thing or two,
           Said that he would surely like the place!
      Whoa! And he went back to the town of Hackensack
        With a very funny look upon his face!

2.   He went into a restaurant, to get a bite to eat,
      With a little bunch of whiskers on his chin;
   He was as welcome in there as he was out in the street,
      With his little bunch of whiskers on his chin;
   He ate a plate of pork and beans, and when he went to pay,
   The man charg'd him five dollars; "That's too much," old Rube did say
   "I know it is," the man said, "but I need the cash to-day."
   And he pulled the little whiskers on his chin.

   Chorus: Reuben Glue got the huckleberry doo,
           Said he knew he wouldn't like the place!
      Whoa! And he went back to the town of Hackensack,
        With a very funny look upon his face!

3.   Into a poker game he sat, to pass the time away,
      With a little bunch of whiskers on his chin;

A "Jackpot" it was opened and old Reuben says, "I'll stay."
   With his little bunch of whiskers on his chin;
And when it came to drawing cards, old Reuben he took one!
Says he, "I'll show these city sharps a little bit of fun!"
Old Reuben held four aces, but the sharper held a gun
   At the little bunch of whiskers on his chin.
Chorus: Reuben Glue from the table quickly flew,
      Said he knew he wouldn't like the place!
   Whoa! And he went back to the town of Hackensack,
      With a very funny look upon his face!

4. He went into a beer saloon, to try and quench his thirst,
   With a little bunch of whiskers on his chin;
The gang inside got fighting about which one saw him first,
   With his little bunch of whiskers on his chin;
They nail'd his shoes down to the floor, he couldn't get away,
For all the drinks they had that night, old Reuben had to pay.
They pulled his leg so hard, he had to buy a crutch next day,
   Also had to cut the whiskers off his chin.
Chorus: Reuben Glue didn't do a thing to you,
      Said he knew he wouldn't like the place!
   Whoa! Then he hopped back to the town of Hackensack,
      But he hadn't any whiskers on his face!

One of the most famous "Reuben" songs, of course, is *Reuben and Rachel*, but this really has nothing to do with farmers. It is a dialogue, starting "Reuben, Reuben, I've been thinking," in which the two characters disagree until the final verse, when Reuben asks Rachel to be his wife "And I'll split with you my money every pay-day of my life." There is also little of the rural atmosphere in that song about "Reuben and that little maid" who were "On their Honeymoon."[2]

Miss Katharine Lane, who, after years of urbanizing, is still a country mouse at heart, contributes from an amazing memory this delightful reminiscence of the days when lightning-rods were lightning-rods:

I'm a jolly old farmer, Ben Hastings is my name,
I come way down from Skowhicken, Maine.

Got forty acres of well-tilled land,
A barn full of hay and a bank full of sand

---

[1] On the third chorus sing, "I'll be durned, the butter ain't churned."

[2] Such songs as *The Bowery* transplanted the traditional "rube" to the city, invariably with disastrous effect, but they do not belong to the rural school, and their attitude is always sophisticated and often contemptuous.

Forty head of cattle and one big shoat,
Ten head of horses and a billy-goat.

Out in the garden, pulling up sod,
Along come a lady with a lightnin'-rod.

Slicker than a mink, quicker than a mouse,
Wanted to put the lightnin'-rod over our house.

"Put it all over, I don't care."
She put it all over, I dee-clare.

Five hundred dollars was her fee.
Sez I, "The house don't belong to me!"

HAS ANYBODY HERE SEEN KELLY?

The Kelly song, one of the greatest of the "spelling" type
(*Harrigan* and *Mississippi* are its closest rivals) has quite a history
which its American adapter, William J. McKenna, lives to tell
with the smile and the hair and the eyes of Kelly himself. The
song was originally English, written by C. W. Murphy and Will
Letters, and it dealt with an Irishman from the Isle of Man, who
was taken in hand by a lady of leisure, only to leave her for a rival.
Its forerunner had been a song about one Antonio, a hokey-pokey
ice-cream merchant, who played his benefactress a similar trick.
When Emma Carus sang the original *Kelly*, it contained the lines:

> He's as bad as old Antonio,
> He left me upon my ownio.

This couplet, which was a "wow" in England, with the reference to
the Isle of Man, naturally meant nothing to an American audience,
and Kelly was a "flop" until McKenna made it over for Nora
Bayes, who sang it to instantaneous success in "The Jolly Bache-
lors."

It is worth noting that the verse of the Kelly song was later
copied literally for the verse of *Tipperary*, while that popular war-
song borrowed its chorus from an Irish ballad, *Eileen Alanna*,
which was sung here many years before by Tony Pastor.   Every-

body knows the music of *Has Anybody Here Seen Kelly?* but how about the words?

> Michael Kelly with his sweetheart come from County Cork
> And bent upon a holiday, they landed in New York.
> They strolled around to see the sights, alas, it's sad to say,
> Poor Kelly lost his little girl upon the Great White Way,
> She walked uptown from Herald Square to Forty-second Street,
> The traffic stopped as she cried to the copper on the beat:
>
> *Chorus:* Has anybody here seen Kelly?
> K E double L Y,
> Has anybody here seen Kelly?
> Have you seen him smile?
> Sure his hair is red, his eyes are blue,
> And he's Irish through and through,
> Has anybody here seen Kelly?
> Kelly from the Emerald Isle.
>
> Over on Fifth Avenue, a band began to play,
> Ten thousand men were marching for it was Saint Patrick's Day,
> The "Wearing of the Green" rang out upon the morning air,
> 'Twas Kelly's fav'rite song, so Mary said, "I'll find him there."
> She climbed upon the grand stand in hopes her Mike she'd see,
> Five hundred Kellys left the ranks in answer to her plea: *[Chorus]*

THE CURSE OF AN ACHING HEART

"You can't go wrong with any Feist song" is the slogan of the publishers of *The Curse of an Aching Heart,* so let's omit all embarrassing questions concerning its plot. It was the last of those delicate ballads dealing with "the facts of life," and it achieved wide popularity, with the full approval of the Sumners and the Comstocks.

Henry Fink (not the lamented music critic) wrote the words, and the music is by Al Piantadosi. All join in the chorus:

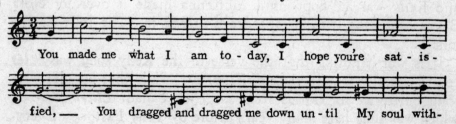

You made me what I am to-day, I hope you're sat-is-

fied, —— You dragged and dragged me down un-til My soul with-

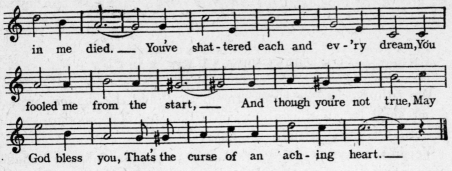

in me died. — You've shat-tered each and ev-'ry dream, You fooled me from the start, — And though you're not true, May God bless you, That's the curse of an ach-ing heart. —

With such a splendid example of tolerance this book may well come to a close. The methods of expression may have varied with passing decades, but the materials of popular American song literature have been fairly constant.

Like all the folk-music, the modern lyrics of the people have kept in touch with current events. The Neapolitans celebrated the completion of the funicular railway up Vesuvius with *Funiculi, Funicula*, and the arrival of the telephone also claimed its troubadour. In this country and century, however, we are guilty of *They Needed a Songbird in Heaven, so God Took Caruso Away*, and, quite recently, *There's a New Star in Heaven, To-night* (dedicated to the late Rudolph Valentino). If we must have personalities, such a song as *Trudy* seems infinitely preferable.

P.S.—TWENTY YEARS LATER

WE THOUGHT we were moderns in 1925, and the chances are we never shall be all that that word connotes. The modernism of yesterday is the platitude of today.

Yet in the past twenty years America's popular music has made such definite advances that it no longer deserves either a patronizing or a pitying approach. Tin Pan Alley still turns out its full quota of nonsense, bathos, vulgarity and dullness, but all of this drivel is more than balanced by an increasing volume of utterly charming words and music, literate, adult and thoroughly expressive of America as it is at present.

Most of this new output is lumped under the professional title of "production numbers," with motion pictures now adding more and more to the material of the legitimate musical theatre. The three men who have contributed most significantly to this higher standard of popular music are the late George Gershwin, Jerome Kern and Richard Rodgers, with considerable co-operation from such composers as Cole Porter, Irving Berlin, Vincent Youmans, Vernon Duke, Sigmund Romberg, Rudolph Friml, Arthur Schwartz and Kurt Weill.

America's popular songs since 1925 have followed the old patterns to some extent, but with a new sophistication and a decided improvement in the technique of both versification and musicianship. The chief distinction today is between "ballads" and "novelty songs," the former term covering practically everything of a frankly sentimental nature, while the latter applies to any idiosyncrasy from a twist of current slang to the lingual absurdities of *Mairzy Doats.*

A mere listing of the hits of the past twenty years would take up more room than is here available, so let's be content with touching only the high spots. Obviously many of the statements in the preceding chapter have already been proved wrong. The phonograph record business has come back with a bang, and the chief problem today is to supply the demand, not only for popular discs but for albums of the classics.

Radio did cut down the sale of sheet-music, but it has nevertheless proved the quickest and most effective medium for plugging a song into national success. A rousing hit no longer sells a million copies or more; half that number is about the limit today. But publishers can bring out more numbers in a given time and make a quick turn-over, without worrying about length of life.

The novelties and the overnight successes need not be taken seriously in this Coda to a definitely non-serious book. But consider the remarkable consistency with which our leaders in popular song-writing have turned out solid hits, many of which have already won the distinction of a "standard" label, which implies as much permanence as Tin Pan Alley can afford to recognize. It is interesting also to note the number of successful revivals in recent years, and here again both radio and the screen have been of real help.

George Gershwin had his first hit, *Swanee*, as early as 1919, and he continued to turn them out with great regularity until his untimely death in 1937. His best song is probably *The Man I Love*, which uses the old blue sequence to form a haunting melody, with a descending chromatic scale for a countertheme. But such titles as *Liza*, *Do-do-do*, *Someone to Watch Over Me*, *Embraceable You*, *Stairway to Paradise*, *Strike Up the Band* and *I Got Rhythm* are not likely to be forgotten. Meanwhile their composer made serious musical history with his *Rhapsody in Blue*, *Piano Concerto*, *An American in Paris* and the opera, *Porgy and Bess*, which itself contained several popular hits.

Jerome Kern was already an old hand at musical comedy in 1925, when his *Sunny* introduced *Who?* and several other smashes. *Show Boat* came two years later, with the immortal *Old Man River*, as well as *Bill*, *Make Believe*, *Why Do I Love You?* and a few others. *Roberta*, whose cast included a young man named Bob Hope, contained *Smoke Gets in Your Eyes*, which seems to be Mr. Kern's own favorite. But he topped this classic with *All the Things You Are*, not to speak of *The Last Time I Saw Paris* and the recent *Long Ago and Far Away*.

Richard Rodgers burst upon the musical world in 1925, when, with Lorenz Hart as lyricist, he contributed to the *Garrick Gaieties* such gems as *Manhattan* and *Mountain Greenery*, closely followed by *Dearest Enemy*, with *Here in My Arms* and other hits. *The Girl Friend* (1926) contained not only the clever title song, but also *The Blue Room*. Later came *Thou Swell, My Heart Stood Still, Ten Cents a Dance*, etc. At one time Rodgers and Hart had three hit shows running simultaneously on Broadway, *The Boys from Syracuse, I'd Rather Be Right* and *I Married an Angel*. After Larry Hart's death, Rodgers teamed up with Oscar Hammerstein II and they immediately hit the jackpot with *Oklahoma!*, a show without a weak number in it, the high lights being *Oh, What A Beautiful Morning!, People Will Say We're in Love* and the *Surrey with a Fringe on Top*. Now there is also *Carousel*, with *If I Loved You* and other delightful combinations of Rodgers music and Hammerstein words.

The case of Irving Berlin is unique, because he has written both his lyrics and his tunes for nearly forty years and still seems just as good as ever. The middle twenties were his sentimental period, when he created ballads like *All Alone, What'll I Do?, Always* (successfully revived twenty years later), *Remember?* and *Because I Love You*. With *Blue Skies, Easter Parade, Cheek to Cheek* and other hits filling the intervening years, Berlin came out in 1940 with *God Bless America*, originally written in 1917 but discarded then as too serious. *This is the Army* contained several good numbers, besides contributing enormously to the war effort, and *White Christmas* provided what may prove the climax of Berlin's career, bringing back the tradition of sales in the millions and permanently established as a Yuletide standard.

Cole Porter also has the gift of writing both words and music, with a sophisticated touch that marked such early hits as *Love for Sale* and *What Is This Thing Called Love?*, eventually arriving at *Night and Day, I've Got You Under My Skin, Begin the Beguine*,

You're the Top and *I Get a Kick Out of You*. Sigmund Romberg has been content to supply singable melodies for such operettas as the *Desert Song, New Moon* and *Student Prince*, with Franz Schubert helping him out in *Blossom Time*. One of his great individual hits is *When I Grow Too Old to Dream*.

Arthur Schwartz, now a Hollywood producer, has *Dancing in the Dark* and other successes to his credit, with Howard Dietz his regular lyricist. Vincent Youmans scored with *Hit the Deck, Great Day* and other shows, while Vernon Duke came into his own in *Cabin in the Sky*, written with John LaTouche. The outstanding successes of Kurt Weill, *Lady in The Dark* and *One Touch of Venus*, are still current. Hoagy Carmichael's *Star Dust*; Neil Moret's *Chloe*; Mabel Wayne's *Ramona*; the de Rose-Parish *Deep Purple*; *Stormy Weather*; the Noel Coward waltzes; *Thanks for the Memory*; *The Last Round-up* and other Billy Hill hits; *Intermezzo* and *The White Cliffs of Dover* are worth mentioning among the deservedly popular songs that have shown some lasting quality.

Yes, We Have No Bananas still sets the standard for nonsense, but it has had strong rivals in *The Music Goes Round and Round*, the *Hut Sut Song, Three Little Fishes, Pistol Packin' Mama* and *Mairzy Doats*. Meanwhile an incredible record was made by that classic of hill-billy patriotism, *There's a Star Spangled Banner Waving Somewhere*. Obviously the end is not yet.

INDEX OF SONG TITLES

An Album of
ELEGANT ART

Including delightfully decorated covers of some

sentimental songs of cherished fame — With pretty

pictures of their irresistible interpreters — And

some scenes of love romantic and demure — All a

nosegay of nostalgic memories

❧ INVOCATION ❧

Sing like they used to in Grandpapa's time,
Don't think of grammar or rhyming each line,
Drag in poor Mother and white-nightied tots,
Wronged ladies, gold-slaves, in nice sorted lots.
Maudlin, macabre, let death be your joy,
Sigh sentimentally! Whoops! Attaboy!
Go get that urn, kid, across the dark tarn,
Put in some naughty words, "devil" or "darn."
Tickle that lute, it's a beaut'! Toot, toot!
Taking a boat or a train would be cute—
Any old place with a "home town" appeal,
Lyric geography needn't be real.
Get up some dialect, Irish or Dutch,
Jokes done in black-face don't have to be much.
Jump in the slush-pond, it ain't very deep!
Songs haven't changed a lot! "Read 'em and Weep!"

THE FATHER OF THEM ALL
(Proving also that the Charleston was danced in 1815)

SENTIMENTALITY WITH A CAPITAL S
A Pleasing Melancholy and a Melancholy Pleasure Combined

WAS THAT CROQUET?

Nay, Rather, a Game of Hearts

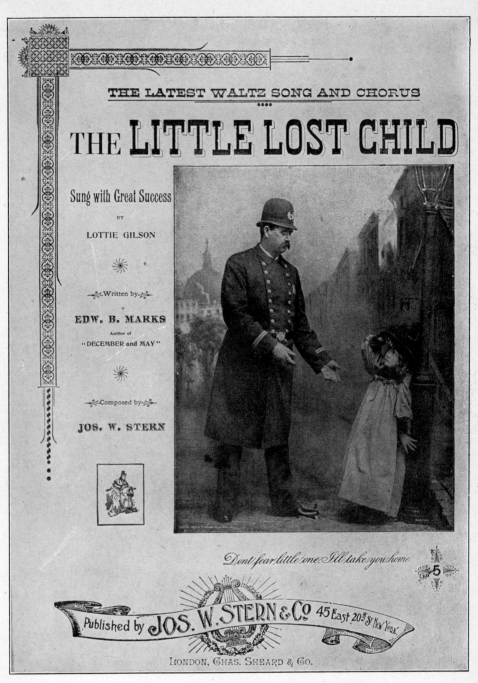

A Classic of the Rogers Group Period
This Typical Cover Shows a Bit of Old New York

A passing policeman found a little child.   *At the station when he asked her for her name.*   *"Your little features bring back her dear face."*

"You were a babe in arms when your mother left me one day."   *Husband and wife then meeting face to face.*   *"No more from me (us) shall you roam."*

The First of the Song Slides
Introducing "The Little Lost Child" to the Screen of 1894

Streamlined for Speed

FLIRTING ON THE ICE   TWILIGHT IN THE PARK

The Seasons Change, but Lovers are the Same

TWO PLANTATION MELODIES!   STANDARD AND POPULAR!

CARRY ME BACK TO OLD VIRGINNY.

Song and Chorus.   Words and Music by James A. Bland.   40.

THERE'S A HAPPY LITTLE HOME.

Song and Chorus.   Words and Music by Harry Woodson.   40.

BOSTON:

PUBLISHED BY JOHN F. PERRY & CO., 13 WEST STREET,

4 doors from Washington.

New York: W. A. POND & CO., 25 Union Square.

Be it ever so humble . . .

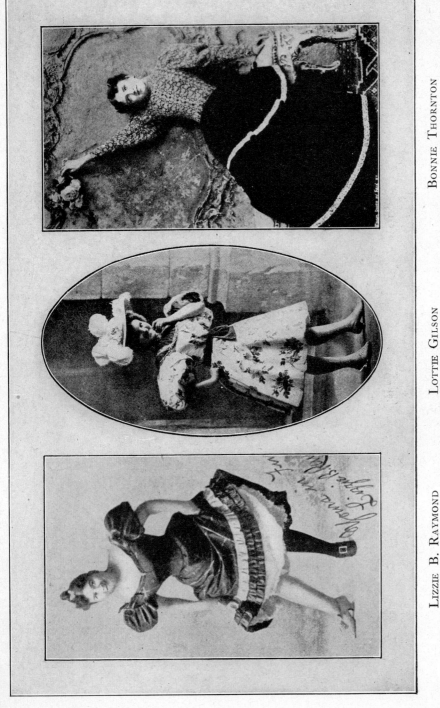

LIZZIE B. RAYMOND   LOTTIE GILSON   BONNIE THORNTON

Three Irresistible Interpreters of the Nineties

The Gallant Seems to be Headed the Wrong Way

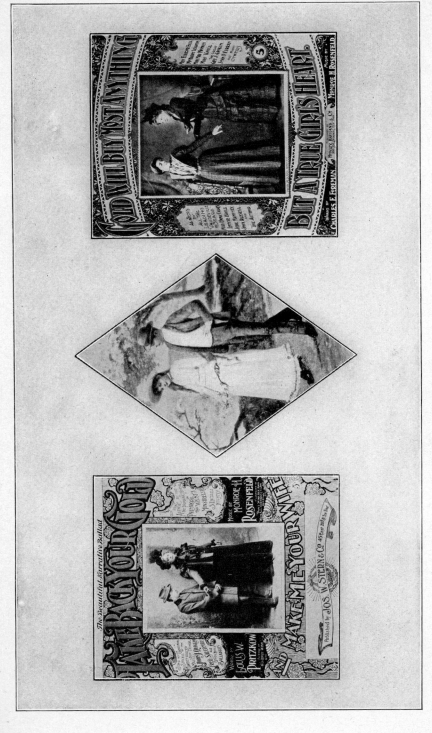

FAVOURITE TOPICS AND TITLES OF THE GOLDEN AGE

Rural Sweetness and Light vs. the Sophistication of the Great City

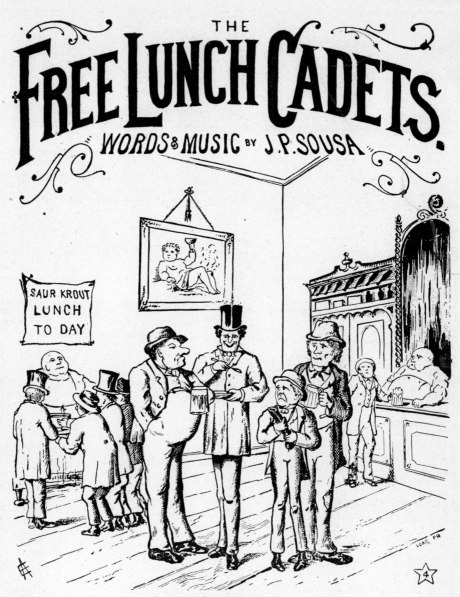

PROHIBITION'S ARTFUL AID
Mr. Sousa Does His Bit for Temperance

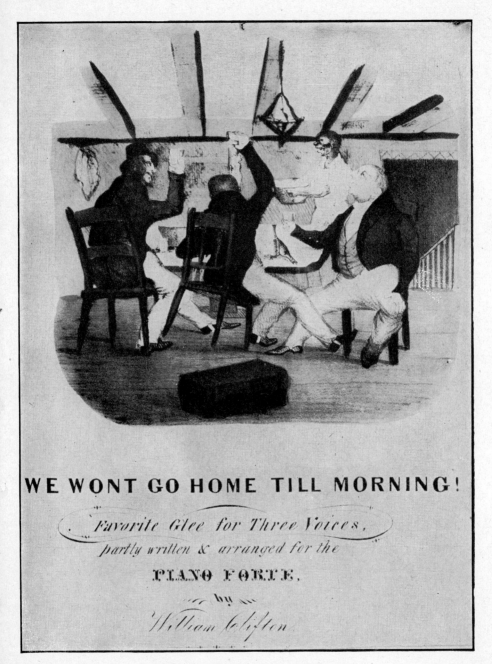

WE WONT GO HOME TILL MORNING!

Favorite Glee for Three Voices,
partly written & arranged for the

PIANO FORTE,

by

William Clifton

Only the Clothes Have Changed

❧ EXHORTATION ❧

*

Princess or Prince (to be perfectly fair with all
Those who for purchasing books have the wherewithal)
If you have read them and wept, as you should,
Maybe you think those old songs were no good?
Reader, the public has always forgotten
Things that were utterly useless and rotten;
Somewhere in nature there must be a reason
Why the same crop should come up every season.
Think you by chance that our forefathers spent all
Human capacity pro-sentimental?
Look at the songs that are rampant to-day!
Sentimentality still shows the way.
"Petting" and "necking" are new words for "spooning,"
Lovers galore are still mooning and crooning,
Stage clocks and vaudeville watches perhaps tick
Less than before to the beat of the slap-stick,
But the comedian still gets his laughter
Much as he did in the 'Eighties and after.
Grammar and rhetoric still are neglected.
Assonance rather than rhyme is respected.
Tunes are so plentiful, why should a fellow de-
Spair of composing a popular melody?
Princess, or Prince, do you want to feel cheap?
Look up the latest hits!   Read 'em and Weep!

THE END